Glencoe McGraw-Hill

Chapter 10 Resource Masters

Geometry

McGraw Hill Glencoe

Consumable Workbooks Many of the worksheets contained in the Chapter Resource Masters are available as consumable workbooks in both English and Spanish.

	ISBN10	ISBN13
Study Guide and Intervention Workbook	0-07-890848-5	978-0-07-890848-4
Homework Practice Workbook	0-07-890849-3	978-0-07-890849-1

Spanish Versions

Homework Practice Workbook	0-07-890853-1	978-0-07-890853-8

Answers for Workbooks The answers for Chapter 10 of these workbooks can be found in the back of this Chapter Resource Masters booklet.

StudentWorks Plus™ This CD-ROM includes the entire Student Edition text along with the English workbooks listed above.

TeacherWorks Plus™ All of the materials found in this booklet are included for viewing, printing, and editing in this CD-ROM.

Spanish Assessment Masters (ISBN10: 0-07-890856-6, ISBN13: 978-0-07-890856-9) These masters contain a Spanish version of Chapter 10 Test Form 2A and Form 2C.

The *McGraw·Hill* Companies

Mc Graw Hill **Glencoe**

Send all inquiries to:
Glencoe/McGraw-Hill
8787 Orion Place
Columbus, OH 43240-4027

ISBN: 978-0-07-890519-3
MHID: 0-07-890519-2

Printed in the United States of America.

4 5 6 7 8 9 10 REL 14 13 12 11

Contents

Teacher's Guide to Using the
Chapter 10 Resource Masters

The *Chapter 10 Resource Masters* includes the core materials needed for Chapter 10. These materials include worksheets, extensions, and assessment options. The answers for these pages appear at the back of this booklet.

All of the materials found in this booklet are included for viewing and printing on the *TeacherWorks Plus*™ CD-ROM.

Chapter Resources

Student-Built Glossary (pages 1–2) These masters are a student study tool that presents up to twenty of the key vocabulary terms from the chapter. Students are to record definitions and/or examples for each term. You may suggest that students highlight or star the terms with which they are not familiar. Give this to students before beginning Lesson 10-1. Encourage them to add these pages to their mathematics study notebooks. Remind them to complete the appropriate words as they study each lesson.

Anticipation Guide (pages 3–4) This master, presented in both English and Spanish, is a survey used before beginning the chapter to pinpoint what students may or may not know about the concepts in the chapter. Students will revisit this survey after they complete the chapter to see if their perceptions have changed.

Lesson Resources

Study Guide and Intervention These masters provide vocabulary, key concepts, additional worked-out examples and Check Your Progress exercises to use as a reteaching activity. It can also be used in conjunction with the Student Edition as an instructional tool for students who have been absent.

Skills Practice This master focuses more on the computational nature of the lesson. Use as an additional practice option or as homework for second-day teaching of the lesson.

Practice This master closely follows the types of problems found in the Exercises section of the Student Edition and includes word problems. Use as an additional practice option or as homework for second-day teaching of the lesson.

Word Problem Practice This master includes additional practice in solving word problems that apply the concepts of the lesson. Use as an additional practice or as homework for second-day teaching of the lesson.

Enrichment These activities may extend the concepts of the lesson, offer a historical or multicultural look at the concepts, or widen students' perspectives on the mathematics they are learning. They are written for use with all levels of students.

Graphing Calculator or Spreadsheet Activities These activities present ways in which technology can be used with the concepts in some lessons of this chapter. Use as an alternative approach to some concepts or as an integral part of your lesson presentation.

Assessment Options

The assessment masters in the *Chapter 10 Resource Masters* offer a wide range of assessment tools for formative (monitoring) assessment and summative (final) assessment.

Student Recording Sheet This master corresponds with the standardized test practice at the end of the chapter.

Extended-Response Rubric This master provides information for teachers and students on how to assess performance on open-ended questions.

Quizzes Four free-response quizzes offer assessment at appropriate intervals in the chapter.

Mid-Chapter Test This 1-page test provides an option to assess the first half of the chapter. It parallels the timing of the Mid-Chapter Quiz in the Student Edition and includes both multiple-choice and free-response questions.

Vocabulary Test This test is suitable for all students. It includes a list of vocabulary words and 10 questions to assess students' knowledge of those words. This can also be used in conjunction with one of the leveled chapter tests.

Leveled Chapter Tests

- **Form 1** contains multiple-choice questions and is intended for use with below grade level students.

- **Forms 2A and 2B** contain multiple-choice questions aimed at on grade level students. These tests are similar in format to offer comparable testing situations.

- **Forms 2C and 2D** contain free-response questions aimed at on grade level students. These tests are similar in format to offer comparable testing situations.

- **Form 3** is a free-response test for use with above grade level students.

All of the above mentioned tests include a free-response Bonus question.

Extended-Response Test Performance assessment tasks are suitable for all students. Sample answers and a scoring rubric are included for evaluation.

Standardized Test Practice These three pages are cumulative in nature. It includes three parts: multiple-choice questions with bubble-in answer format, griddable questions with answer grids, and short-answer free-response questions.

Answers

- The answers for the Anticipation Guide and Lesson Resources are provided as reduced pages.

- Full-size answer keys are provided for the assessment masters.

10 Student-Built Glossary

This is an alphabetical list of the key vocabulary terms you will learn in Chapter 10. As you study the chapter, complete each term's definition or description. Remember to add the page number where you found the term. Add these pages to your Geometry Study Notebook to review vocabulary at the end of the chapter.

Vocabulary Term	Found on Page	Definition/Description/Example
arc		
center		
central angle		
chord		
circle		

(continued on the next page)

Chapter Resources

10 Student-Built Glossary (continued)

Vocabulary Term	Found on Page	Definition/Description/Example
circumference		
diameter		
pi (π)		
radius		

10 Anticipation Guide

Circles and Circumference

Step 1	Before you begin Chapter 10

- Read each statement.
- Decide whether you Agree (A) or Disagree (D) with the statement.
- Write A or D in the first column OR if you are not sure whether you agree or disagree, write NS (Not Sure).

STEP 1 A, D, or NS	Statement	STEP 2 A or D
	1. The distance from any point on a circle to the center of the circle is called the diameter.	
	2. A chord of a circle is any segment with endpoints that are on the circle.	
	3. The formula for the circumference of a circle is $C = \pi r^2$.	
	4. The vertex of a central angle of a circle is at the center of the circle.	
	5. If two arcs from two different circles have the same measure then the arcs are congruent.	
	6. In a circle, two minor arcs are congruent if their corresponding chords are congruent.	
	7. In a circle, two chords that are equidistant from the center are congruent.	
	8. The measure of an inscribed angle equals the measure of its intercepted arc.	
	9. A line is tangent to a circle only if it contains a chord of the circle.	
	10. Two secant lines of a circle can intersect in the interior or the exterior of the circle.	
	11. If two chords intersect inside a circle then the two chords are congruent.	
	12. The center of a circle represented by the equation $(x + 3)^2 + (y + 5)^2 = 9$ is located at (3, 5).	

Step 2	After you complete Chapter 10

- Reread each statement and complete the last column by entering an A or a D.
- Did any of your opinions about the statements change from the first column?
- For those statements that you mark with a D, use a piece of paper to write an example of why you disagree.

10 Ejercicios preparatorios

Círculos

Antes de comenzar el Capítulo 10

- Lee cada enunciado.

- Decide si estás de acuerdo (A) o en desacuerdo (D) con el enunciado.

- Escribe A o D en la primera columna O si no estás seguro(a) de la respuesta, escribe NS (No estoy seguro(a)).

PASO 1 A, D o NS	Enunciado	PASO 2 A o D
	1. La distancia desde cualquier punto de un círculo al centro del mismo se llama diámetro.	
	2. La cuerda de un círculo es cualquier segmento cuyos extremos están sobre el círculo.	
	3. La fórmula para la circunferencia del círculo es $C = \pi r^2$.	
	4. El vértice del ángulo central de un círculo está en el centro del círculo.	
	5. Si dos arcos de dos círculos diferentes tienen la misma medida, entonces los arcos son congruentes.	
	6. En un círculo, dos arcos menores son congruentes si sus cuerdas correspondientes son congruentes.	
	7. En un círculo, dos cuerdas que equidistan del centro son congruentes.	
	8. La medida de un ángulo inscrito es igual a la medida de la intersección de su arco.	
	9. Una recta es tangente a un círculo sólo si contiene una cuerda del círculo.	
	10. Dos secantes de un círculo se pueden intersecar en el interior o en el exterior del círculo.	
	11. Si dos cuerdas se intersecan dentro de un círculo, entonces las dos cuerdas son congruentes.	
	12. El centro de un círculo que se representa con la ecuación $(x + 3)^2 + (y + 5)^2 = 9$ se localiza en $(3, 5)$.	

Después de completar el Capítulo 10

- Vuelve a leer cada enunciado y completa la última columna con una A o una D.

- ¿Cambió cualquiera de tus opiniones sobre los enunciados de la primera columna?

- En una hoja de papel aparte, escribe un ejemplo de por qué estás en desacuerdo con los enunciados que marcaste con una D.

10-1 Study Guide and Intervention

Circles and Circumference

Segments in Circles A **circle** consists of all points in a plane that are a given distance, called the **radius**, from a given point called the **center**.

A segment or line can intersect a circle in several ways.

- A segment with endpoints that are at the center and on the circle is a **radius**.
- A segment with endpoints on the circle is a **chord**.
- A chord that passes through the circle's center and made up of collinear radii is a **diameter**.

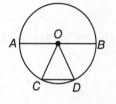

chord: $\overline{AE}$, $\overline{BD}$

radius: $\overline{FB}$, $\overline{FC}$, $\overline{FD}$

diameter: $\overline{BD}$

For a circle that has radius r and diameter d, the following are true

$$r = \frac{d}{2} \qquad\qquad r = \frac{1}{2}d \qquad\qquad d = 2r$$

Example

a. Name the circle.

The name of the circle is $\odot O$.

b. Name radii of the circle.

$\overline{AO}$, $\overline{BO}$, $\overline{CO}$, and $\overline{DO}$ are radii.

c. Name chords of the circle.

$\overline{AB}$ and $\overline{CD}$ are chords.

Exercises

For Exercises 1–7, refer to

1. Name the circle.

2. Name radii of the circle.

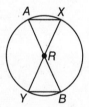

3. Name chords of the circle.

4. Name diameters of the circle.

5. If $AB = 18$ millimeters, find AR.

6. If $RY = 10$ inches, find AR and AB.

7. Is $\overline{AB} \cong \overline{XY}$? Explain.

10-1 Study Guide and Intervention (continued)

Circles and Circumference

Circumference The **circumference** of a circle is the distance around the circle.

Circumference	For a circumference of C units and a diameter of d units of a radius of r units, $C = \pi d$ or $C = 2\pi r$

Example Find the circumference of the circle to the nearest hundredth.

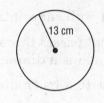

$C = 2\pi r$ Circumference formula

$\quad = 2\pi(13)$ $r = 13$

$\quad = 26\pi$ Simplify.

$\quad \approx 81.68$ Use a calculator.

The circumference is 26π or about 81.68 centimeters.

Exercises

Find the diameter and radius of a circle with the given circumference. Round to the nearest hundredth.

1. $C = 40$ in.

2. $C = 256$ ft

3. $C = 15.62$ m

4. $C = 9$ cm

5. $C = 79.5$ yd

6. $C = 204.16$ m

Find the exact circumference of each circle using the given inscribed or circumscribed polygon.

7.

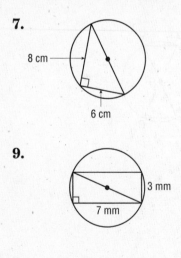

8 cm

6 cm

8.

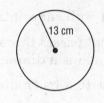

9 in.

9.

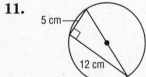

3 mm

7 mm

10.

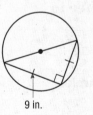

11 yd

11.

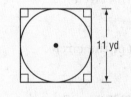

5 cm

12 cm

12.

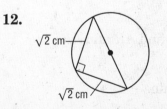

$\sqrt{2}$ cm

$\sqrt{2}$ cm

10-1 Skills Practice

Circles and Circumference

For Exercises 1–7, refer to ⊙P.

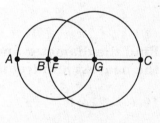

1. Name the circle.

2. Name a radius.

3. Name a chord.

4. Name a diameter.

5. Name a radius not drawn as part of a diameter.

6. Suppose the diameter of the circle is 16 centimeters. Find the radius.

7. If $PC = 11$ inches, find AB.

The diameters of ⊙F and ⊙G are 5 and 6 units, respectively. Find each measure.

8. BF

9. AB

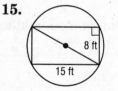

Find the diameter and radius of a circle with the given circumference. Round to the nearest hundredth.

10. $C = 36$ m

11. $C = 17.2$ ft

12. $C = 81.3$ cm

13. $C = 5$ yd

Find the exact circumference of each circle.

14.

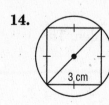

3 cm

15.

8 ft

15 ft

Lesson 10-1

10-1 Practice

Circles and Circumference

For Exercises 1–7, refer to ⊙L.

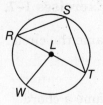

1. Name the circle.

2. Name a radius.

3. Name a chord.

4. Name a diameter.

5. Name a radius not drawn as part of a diameter.

6. Suppose the radius of the circle is 3.5 yards. Find the diameter.

7. If $RT = 19$ meters, find LW.

The diameters of ⊙L and ⊙M are 20 and 13 units, respectively, and $QR = 4$. Find each measure.

8. LQ

9. RM

Find the diameter and radius of a circle with the given circumference. Round to the nearest hundredth.

10. $C = 21.2$ ft

11. $C = 5.9$ m

Find the exact circumference of each circle using the given inscribed or circumscribed polygon.

12.

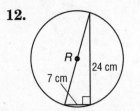

13.

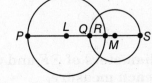

14. SUNDIALS Herman purchased a sundial to use as the centerpiece for a garden. The diameter of the sundial is 9.5 inches.

a. Find the radius of the sundial.

b. Find the circumference of the sundial to the nearest hundredth.

10-1 Word Problem Practice

Circles and Circumference

Copyright © Glencoe/McGraw-Hill, a division of The McGraw-Hill Companies, Inc.

Lesson 10-1

1. **WHEELS** Zack is designing wheels for a concept car. The diameter of the wheel is 18 inches. Zack wants to make spokes in the wheel that run from the center of the wheel to the rim. In other words, each spoke is a radius of the wheel. How long are these spokes?

2. **CAKE CUTTING** Kathy slices through a circular cake. The cake has a diameter of 14 inches. The slice that Kathy made is straight and has a length of 11 inches.

Did Kathy cut along a *radius,* a *diameter,* or a *chord* of the circle?

3. **COINS** Three identical circular coins are lined up in a row as shown.

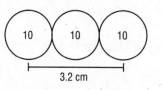

The distance between the centers of the first and third coins is 3.2 centimeters. What is the radius of one of these coins?

4. **PLAZAS** A rectangular plaza has a surrounding circular fence. The diagonals of the rectangle pass from one point on the fence through the center of the circle to another point on the fence.

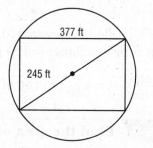

Based on the information in the figure, what is the diameter of the fence? Round your answer to the nearest tenth of a foot.

5. **EXERCISE HOOPS** Taiga wants to make a circular loop that he can twirl around his body for exercise. He will use a tube that is 2.5 meters long.

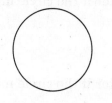

a. What will be the diameter of Taiga's exercise hoop? Round your answer to the nearest thousandth of a meter.

b. What will be the radius of Taiga's exercise hoop? Round your answer to the nearest thousandth of a meter.

10-1 Enrichment

Sectors

The area of a circle is found by using the formula $A = \pi r^2$. A sector is a pie-shaped portion of the circle enclosed by 2 radii and the edge of the circle. A central angle of a sector is an angle whose vertex is at the center of the circle and crosses the circle.

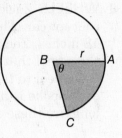

The area of a circle is represented by the formula $A = \pi r^2$. The area of the sector θ is proportional to the part that the central angle is of 360°.

$$\frac{\text{area of sector}}{\text{area of the circle}} = \frac{\theta}{360} \text{ or area of sector} = \frac{\theta}{360}\,\pi r^2.$$

Example   **Find the area of the sector shown at the right.**

$A = \dfrac{\theta}{360}\,\pi r^2$

$A = \dfrac{90}{360}\,\pi(2)^2$ $r = 2, \theta = 90$

$= \dfrac{1}{4}\,(4\pi) \text{ or } \pi$

So the area of the sector is π in^2 or approximately 3.14 square inches.

Exercises

1. Find the area of a sector if the circle has a radius of 10 centimeters and the central angle measures 72.

2. Find the area of a sector if the circle has a radius of 5 inches and the central angle measures 60.

3. If the area of a sector is 15π square centimeters and the radius of the circle is 5 centimeters, find the measure of the central angle.

4. Find the measure of the central angle that intercepts a sector that is $\frac{1}{3}$ the area of the circle.

10-2 Study Guide and Intervention
Measuring Angles and Arcs

Angles and Arcs A **central angle** is an angle whose vertex is at the center of a circle and whose sides are radii. A central angle separates a circle into two arcs, a **major arc** and a **minor arc**.

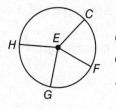

$\overarc{GF}$ is a minor arc.

$\overarc{CHG}$ is a major arc.

$\angle GEF$ is a central angle.

Here are some properties of central angles and arcs.

- The sum of the measures of the central angles of a circle with no interior points in common is 360.

  $m\angle HEC + m\angle CEF + m\angle FEG + m\angle GEH = 360$

- The measure of a minor arc is less than 180 and equal to the measure of its central angle.

  $m\overarc{CF} = m\angle CEF$

- The measure of a major arc is 360 minus the measure of the minor arc.

  $m\overarc{CGF} = 360 - m\overarc{CF}$

- The measure of a semicircle is 180.

- Two minor arcs are congruent if and only if their corresponding central angles are congruent.

  $\overarc{CF} \cong \overarc{FG}$ if and only if $\angle CEF \cong \angle FEG$.

- The measure of an arc formed by two adjacent arcs is the sum of the measures of the two arcs. **(Arc Addition Postulate)**

  $m\overarc{CF} + m\overarc{FG} = m\overarc{CG}$

Example $\overline{AC}$ is a diameter of $\odot R$. Find $m\overarc{AB}$ and $m\overarc{ACB}$.

$\angle ARB$ is a central angle and $m\angle ARB = 42$, so $m\overarc{AB} = 42$.
Thus $m\overarc{ACB} = 360 - 42$ or 318.

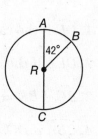

Exercises

Find the value of *x*.

1.

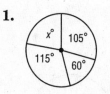

2.

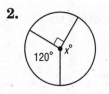

$\overline{BD}$ and $\overline{AC}$ **are diameters of** $\odot O$. **Identify each arc as a** *major arc, minor arc,* **or** *semicircle* **of the circle. Then find its measure.**

3. $m\overarc{BA}$ **4.** $m\overarc{BC}$

5. $m\overarc{CD}$ **6.** $m\overarc{ACB}$

7. $m\overarc{BCD}$ **8.** $m\overarc{AD}$

Lesson 10-2

10-2 **Study Guide and Intervention** (continued)

Measuring Angles and Arcs

Arc Length An arc is part of a circle and its length is a part of the circumference of the circle.

The length of arc ℓ can be found using the following equation:

$\ell = \dfrac{x}{360} \cdot 2\pi r$

Example **Find the length of $\widehat{AB}$. Round to the nearest hundredth.**

The length of arc $\widehat{AB}$, can be found using the following equation: $\widehat{AB} = \dfrac{x}{360} \cdot 2\pi r$

$\widehat{AB} = \dfrac{x}{360} \cdot 2\pi r$	Arc Length Equation
$\widehat{AB} = \dfrac{135}{360} \cdot 2\pi(8)$	Substitution
$\widehat{AB} \approx 18.85$ in.	Use a calculator.

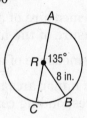

Exercises

Use $\odot O$ to find the length of each arc. Round to the nearest hundredth.

1. $\widehat{DE}$ if the radius is 2 meters

2. $\widehat{DEA}$ if the diameter is 7 inches

3. $\widehat{BC}$ if BE = 24 feet

4. $\widehat{CBA}$ if DO = 3 millimeters

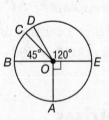

Use $\odot P$ to find the length of each arc. Round to the nearest hundredth.

5. $\widehat{RT}$, if MT = 7 yards

6. $\widehat{MR}$, if PR = 13 feet

7. $\widehat{MST}$, if MP = 2 inches

8. $\widehat{MRS}$, if PS = 10 centimeters

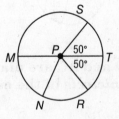

10-2 Skills Practice

Measuring Angles and Arcs

$\overline{AC}$ and $\overline{EB}$ are diameters of $\odot R$. Identify each arc as a *major arc*, *minor arc*, or *semicircle* of the circle. Then find its measure.

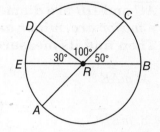

1. $m\widehat{EA}$

2. $m\widehat{CB}$

3. $m\widehat{DC}$

4. $m\widehat{DEB}$

5. $m\widehat{AB}$

6. $m\widehat{CDA}$

$\overline{PR}$ and $\overline{QT}$ are diameters of $\odot A$. Find each measure.

7. $m\widehat{UPQ}$

8. $m\widehat{PQR}$

9. $m\widehat{UTS}$

10. $m\widehat{RS}$

11. $m\widehat{RSU}$

12. $m\widehat{STP}$

13. $m\widehat{PQS}$

14. $m\widehat{PRU}$

Use $\odot D$ to find the length of each arc. Round to the nearest hundredth.

15. $\widehat{LM}$ if the radius is 5 inches

16. $\widehat{MN}$ if the diameter is 3 yards

17. $\widehat{KL}$ if $JD = 7$ centimeters

18. $\widehat{NJK}$ if $NL = 12$ feet

19. $\widehat{KLM}$ if $DM = 9$ millimeters

20. $\widehat{JK}$ if $KD = 15$ inches

Lesson 10-2

10-2 Practice

Measuring Angles and Arcs

$\overline{AC}$ and $\overline{DB}$ are diameters of $\odot Q$. Identify each arc as a *major arc*, *minor arc*, or *semicircle* of the circle. Then find its measure.

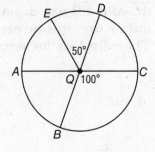

1. $m\widehat{AE}$

2. $m\widehat{AB}$

3. $m\widehat{EDC}$

4. $m\widehat{ADC}$

5. $m\widehat{ABC}$

6. $m\widehat{BC}$

$\overline{FH}$ and $\overline{EG}$ are diameters of $\odot P$. Find each measure.

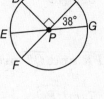

7. $m\widehat{EF}$

8. $m\widehat{DE}$

9. $m\widehat{FG}$

10. $m\widehat{DHG}$

11. $m\widehat{DFG}$

12. $m\widehat{DGE}$

Use $\odot Z$ to find each arc length. Round to the nearest hundredth.

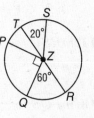

13. $\widehat{QPT}$, if $QZ = 10$ inches

14. $\widehat{QR}$, if $PZ = 12$ feet

15. $\widehat{PQR}$, if $TR = 15$ meters

16. $\widehat{QPS}$, if $ZQ = 7$ centimeters

17. **HOMEWORK** Refer to the table, which shows the number of hours students at Leland High School say they spend on homework each night.

Homework	
Less than 1 hour	8%
1–2 hours	29%
2–3 hours	58%
3–4 hours	3%
Over 4 hours	2%

a. If you were to construct a circle graph of the data, how many degrees would be allotted to each category?

b. Describe the arcs associated with each category.

10-2 Word Problem Practice

Measuring Angles and Arcs

1. **CONDIMENTS** A number of people in a park were asked to name their favorite condiment for hot dogs. The results are shown in the circle graph.

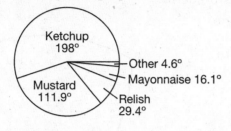

Ketchup 198°
Other 4.6°
Mayonnaise 16.1°
Mustard 111.9°
Relish 29.4°

What was the second most popular hot dog condiment?

2. **CLOCKS** Shiatsu is a Japanese massage technique. One of the beliefs is that various body functions are most active at various times during the day. To illustrate this, they use a Chinese clock that is based on a circle divided into 12 equal sections by radii.

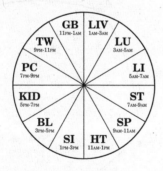

GB 11PM-1AM
LIV 1AM-3AM
TW 9PM-11PM
LU 3AM-5AM
PC 7PM-9PM
LI 5AM-7AM
KID 5PM-7PM
ST 7AM-9AM
BL 3PM-5PM
SP 9AM-11AM
SI 1PM-3PM
HT 11AM-1PM

What is the measure of any one of the 12 equal central angles?

3. **PIES** Yolanda has divided a circular apple pie into 4 slices by cutting the pie along 4 radii. The central angles of the 4 slices are $3x$, $6x - 10$, $4x + 10$, and $5x$ degrees. What exactly are the numerical measures of the central angles?

4. **RIBBONS** Cora is wrapping a ribbon around a cylinder-shaped gift box. The box has a diameter of 15 inches and the ribbon is 60 inches long. Cora is able to wrap the ribbon all the way around the box once, and then continue so that the second end of the ribbon passes the first end. What is the central angle formed between the ends of the ribbon? Round your answer to the nearest tenth of a degree.

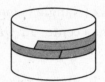

5. **BIKE WHEELS** Lucy has to buy a new wheel for her bike. The bike wheel has a diameter of 20 inches.

a. If Lucy rolls the wheel one complete rotation along the ground, how far will the wheel travel? Round your answer to the nearest hundredth of an inch.

b. If the bike wheel is rolled along the ground so that it rotates 45°, how far will the wheel travel? Round your answer to the nearest hundredth of an inch.

c. If the bike wheel is rolled along the ground for 10 inches, through what angle does the wheel rotate? Round your answer to the nearest tenth of a degree.

Lesson 10-2

10-2 Enrichment

Curves of Constant Width

A circle is called a curve of constant width because no matter how you turn it, the greatest distance across it is always the same. However, the circle is not the only figure with this property.

The figure at the right is called a Reuleaux triangle.

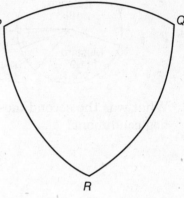

1. Use a metric ruler to find the distance from P to any point on the opposite side.

2. Find the distance from Q to the opposite side.

3. What is the distance from R to the opposite side?

The Reuleaux triangle is made of three arcs. In the example shown, $\overset{\frown}{PQ}$ has center R, $\overset{\frown}{QR}$ has center P, and $\overset{\frown}{PR}$ has center Q.

4. Trace the Reuleaux triangle above on a piece of paper and cut it out. Make a square with sides the length you found in Exercise 1. Show that you can turn the triangle inside the square while keeping its sides in contact with the sides of the square.

5. Make a different curve of constant width by starting with the five points below and following the steps given.

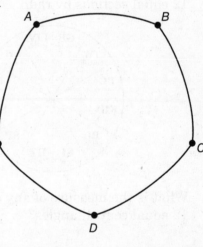

   Step 1: Place the point of your compass on D with opening DA. Make an arc with endpoints A and B.

   Step 2: Make another arc from B to C that has center E.

   Step 3: Continue this process until you have five arcs drawn.

   Some countries use shapes like this for coins. They are useful because they can be distinguished by touch, yet they will work in vending machines because of their constant width.

6. Measure the width of the figure you made in Exercise 5. Draw two parallel lines with the distance between them equal to the width you found. On a piece of paper, trace the five-sided figure and cut it out. Show that it will roll between the lines drawn.

10-3 Study Guide and Intervention

Arcs and Chords

Arcs and Chords Points on a circle determine both chords and arcs. Several properties are related to points on a circle. In a circle or in congruent circles, two minor arcs are congruent if and only if their corresponding chords are congruent.

$\overarc{RS} \cong \overarc{TV}$ if and only if $\overline{RS} \cong \overline{TV}$.

Example In $\odot K$, $\overarc{AB} \cong \overarc{CD}$. Find AB.

$\overarc{AB}$ and $\overarc{CD}$ are congruent arcs, so the corresponding chords $\overline{AB}$ and $\overline{CD}$ are congruent.

$AB = CD$	Definition of congruent segments
$8x = 2x + 3$	Substitution
$x = \dfrac{1}{2}$	Simplify.

So, $AB = 8\left(\dfrac{1}{2}\right)$ or 4.

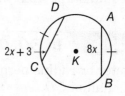

Exercises

ALGEBRA Find the value of x in each circle.

1.

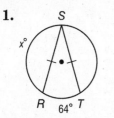

2.

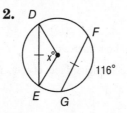

3.

82°

J 4 K

4

L M

x°

4.

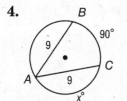

5.

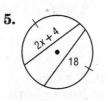

6.

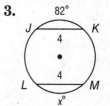

7.

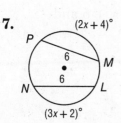

8. $\odot M \cong \odot P$

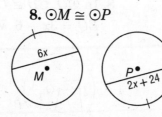

9. $\odot V \cong \odot W$

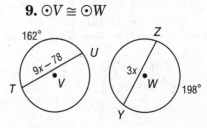

Lesson 10-3

10-3 Study Guide and Intervention (continued)

Arcs and Chords

Diameters and Chords

- In a circle, if a diameter (or radius) is perpendicular to a chord, then it bisects the chord and its arc.

- In a circle, the perpendicular bisector of a chord is the diameter (or radius).

- In a circle or in congruent circles, two chords are congruent if and only if they are equidistant from the center.

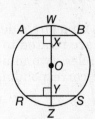

If $\overline{WZ} \perp \overline{AB}$, then $\overline{AX} \cong \overline{XB}$ and $\overarc{AW} \cong \overarc{WB}$.

If $OX = OY$, then $\overline{AB} \cong \overline{RS}$.

If $\overline{AB} \cong \overline{RS}$, then $\overline{AB}$ and $\overline{RS}$ are equidistant from point O.

Example In $\odot O$, $\overline{CD} \perp \overline{OE}$, $OD = 15$, and $CD = 24$. Find OE.

A diameter or radius perpendicular to a chord bisects the chord, so ED is half of CD.

$ED = \frac{1}{2}(24)$
$= 12$

Use the Pythagorean Theorem to find x in $\triangle OED$.

$(OE)^2 + (ED)^2 = (OD)^2$	Pythagorean Theorem
$(OE)^2 + 12^2 = 15^2$	Substitution
$(OE)^2 + 144 = 225$	Simplify.
$(OE)^2 = 81$	Subtract 144 from each side.
$OE = 9$	Take the positive square root of each side.

Exercises

In $\odot P$, the radius is 13 and $RS = 24$. Find each measure. Round to the nearest hundredth.

1. RT 2. PT 3. TQ

In $\odot A$, the diameter is 12, $CD = 8$, and $m\overarc{CD} = 90$. Find each measure. Round to the nearest hundredth.

4. $m\overarc{DE}$ 5. FD 6. AF

7. In $\odot R$, $TS = 21$ and $UV = 3x$. What is x?

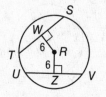

8. In $\odot Q$, $\overline{CD} \cong \overline{CB}$, $GQ = x + 5$ and $EQ = 3x - 6$. What is x?

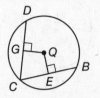

10-3 Skills Practice

Arcs and Chords

ALGEBRA Find the value of x in each circle.

1.

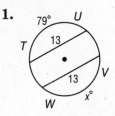

2.

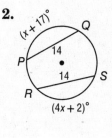

3.

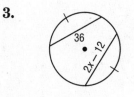

4.

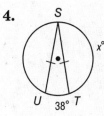

5.

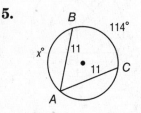

6.

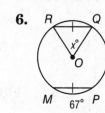

In $\odot Y$ the radius is 34, $AB = 60$, and $m\widehat{AC} = 71$. Find each measure.

7. $m\widehat{BC}$

8. $m\widehat{AB}$

9. AD

10. BD

11. YD

12. DC

13. In $\odot U$, $VW = 20$ and $YZ = 5x$. What is x?

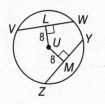

14. In $\odot Z$, $\widehat{TR} \cong \widehat{TV}$, $SZ = x + 4$, and $UZ = 2x - 1$. What is x?

Lesson 10-3

10-3 Practice

Arcs and Chords

ALGEBRA Find the value of x in each circle.

1.

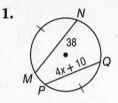

2.

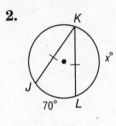

3.

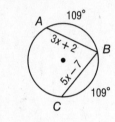

4. $\odot R \cong \odot S$

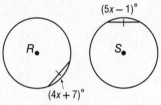

The radius of $\odot N$ is 18, $NK = 9$, and $m\widehat{DE} = 120$. Find each measure.

5. $m\widehat{GE}$

6. $m\angle HNE$

7. $m\angle HEN$

8. HN

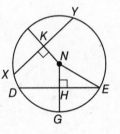

9. In $\odot P$, $QR = 7x - 20$ and $TS = 3x$. What is x?

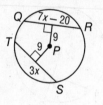

10. In $\odot K$, $\overline{JL} \cong \overline{LM}$, $KN = 3x - 2$, and $KP = 2x + 1$. What is x?

11. GARDEN PATHS A circular garden has paths around its edge that are identified by the given arc measures. It also has four straight paths, identified by segments $\overline{AC}$, $\overline{AD}$, $\overline{BE}$, and $\overline{DE}$, that cut through the garden's interior.
Which two straight paths have the same length?

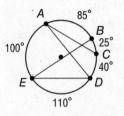

10-3 **Word Problem Practice**

Arcs and Chords

1. HEXAGON A hexagon is constructed as shown in the figure.

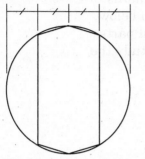

How many different chord lengths occur as side lengths of the hexagon?

2. WATERMARKS For security purposes a jewelry company prints a hidden watermark on the logo of all its official documents. The watermark is a chord located 0.7 cm from the center of a circular ring that has a 2.5 cm radius. To the nearest tenth, what is the length of the chord?

3. ARCHAEOLOGY Only one piece of a broken plate is found during an archaeological dig. Use the sketch of the pottery piece below to demonstrate how constructions with chords and perpendicular bisectors can be used to draw the plate's original size.

4. CENTERS Neil wants to find the center of a large circle. He draws what he thinks is a diameter of the circle and then marks its midpoint and declares that he has found the center. His teacher asks Neil how he knows that the line he drew is the diameter of the circle and not a smaller chord. Neil realizes that he does not know for sure. What can Neil do to determine if it is an actual diameter.

5. QUILTING Miranda is following directions for a quilt pattern "In a 10-inch diameter circle, measure 3 inches from the center of the circle and mark a chord $\overline{AB}$ perpendicular to the radius of the circle. Then cut along the chord." Miranda is to repeat this for another chord, $\overline{CD}$. Finally, she is to cut along chord $\overline{DB}$ and $\overline{AC}$. The result should be four curved pieces and one quadrilateral.

a. If Miranda follows the directions, is she guaranteed that the resulting quadrilateral is a rectangle? Explain.

b. Assume the resulting quadrilateral is a rectangle. One of the curved pieces has an arc measure of 74. What are the measures of the arcs on the other three curved pieces?

Lesson 10-3

10-3 Enrichment

Patterns from Chords

Some beautiful and interesting patterns result if you draw chords to connect evenly spaced points on a circle. On the circle shown below, 24 points have been marked to divide the circle into 24 equal parts. Numbers from 1 to 48 have been placed beside the points. Study the diagram to see exactly how this was done.

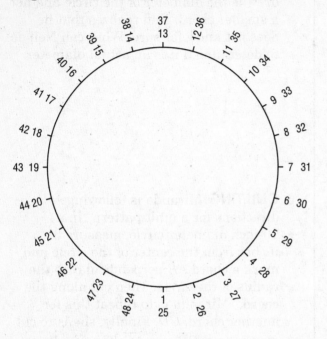

1. Use your ruler and pencil to draw chords to connect numbered points as follows: 1 to 2, 2 to 4, 3 to 6, 4 to 8, and so on. Keep doubling until you have gone all the way around the circle. What kind of pattern do you get?

2. Copy the original circle, points, and numbers. Try other patterns for connecting points. For example, you might try tripling the first number to get the number for the second endpoint of each chord. Keep special patterns for a possible class display.

10-4 Study Guide and Intervention

Inscribed Angles

Inscribed Angles An **inscribed angle** is an angle whose vertex is on a circle and whose sides contain chords of the circle. In $\odot G$, minor arc $\widehat{DF}$ is the **intercepted arc** for inscribed angle $\angle DEF$.

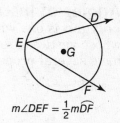

$m\angle DEF = \frac{1}{2}m\widehat{DF}$

Inscribed Angle Theorem	If an angle is inscribed in a circle, then the measure of the angle equals one-half the measure of its intercepted arc.

If two inscribed angles intercept the same arc or congruent arcs, then the angles are congruent.

Example In $\odot G$ above, $m\widehat{DF} = 90$. Find $m\angle DEF$.

$\angle DEF$ is an inscribed angle so its measure is half of the intercepted arc.

$m\angle DEF = \frac{1}{2}m\widehat{DF}$

$\qquad\quad = \frac{1}{2}(90)$ or 45

Exercises

Find each measure.

1. $m\widehat{AC}$

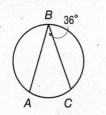

2. $m\angle N$

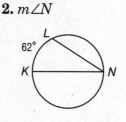

3. $m\widehat{QSR}$

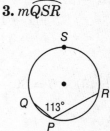

ALGEBRA Find each measure.

4. $m\angle U$

5. $m\angle T$

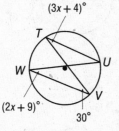

6. $m\angle A$

7. $m\angle C$

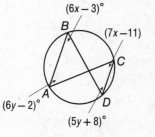

Lesson 10-4

10-4 Study Guide and Intervention (continued)

Inscribed Angles

Angles of Inscribed Polygons An **inscribed polygon** is one whose sides are chords of a circle and whose vertices are points on the circle. Inscribed polygons have several properties.

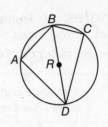

- An inscribed angle of a triangle intercepts a diameter or semicircle if and only if the angle is a right angle.

  If $\overarc{BCD}$ is a semicircle, then $m\angle BCD = 90$.

- If a quadrilateral is inscribed in a circle, then its opposite angles are supplementary.

  For inscribed quadrilateral $ABCD$,
  $m\angle A + m\angle C = 180$ and
  $m\angle ABC + m\angle ADC = 180$.

Example **Find $m\angle K$.**

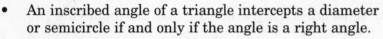

$\overarc{KL} \cong \overarc{KM}$, so $KL = KM$. The triangle is an isosceles triangle, therefore $m\angle L = m\angle M = 3x + 5$.

$$m\angle L + m\angle M + m\angle K = 180 \qquad \text{Angle Sum Theorem}$$
$$(3x + 5) + (3x + 5) + (5x + 5) = 180 \qquad \text{Substitution}$$
$$11x + 15 = 180 \qquad \text{Simplify.}$$
$$11x = 165 \qquad \text{Subtract 15 from each side.}$$
$$x = 15 \qquad \text{Divide each side by 11.}$$

So, $m\angle K = 5(15) + 5 = 80$.

Exercises

ALGEBRA Find each measure.

1. x

2. $m\angle W$

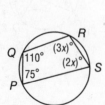

3. x

4. $m\angle T$

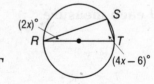

5. $m\angle R$

6. $m\angle S$

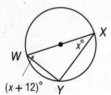

7. $m\angle W$

8. $m\angle X$

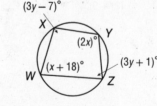

10-4 Skills Practice

Inscribed Angles

Find each measure.

1. $m\widehat{XY}$

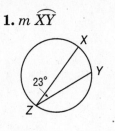

2. $m\angle E$

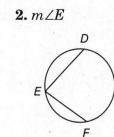

3. $m\angle R$

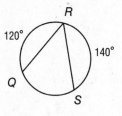

4. $m\widehat{MP}$

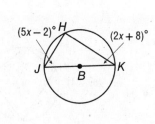

ALGEBRA Find each measure.

5. $m\angle N$

6. $m\angle L$

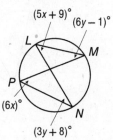

7. $m\angle C$

8. $m\angle A$

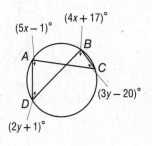

9. $m\angle J$

10. $m\angle K$

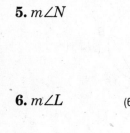

11. $m\angle S$

12. $m\angle R$

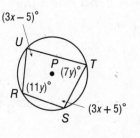

Lesson 10-4

10-4 **Practice**

Inscribed Angles

Find each measure.

1. $m\widehat{AB}$

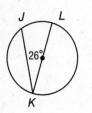

2. $m\angle X$

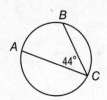

3. $m\widehat{JK}$

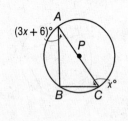

4. $m\angle Q$

ALGEBRA Find each measure.

5. $m\angle W$

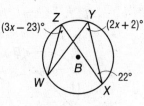

7. $m\angle A$

6. $m\angle Y$

8. $m\angle D$

ALGEBRA Find each measure.

9. $m\angle A$

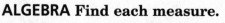

11. $m\angle G$

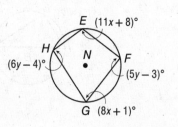

10. $m\angle C$

12. $m\angle H$

13. PROBABILITY In $\odot V$, point C is randomly located so that it does not coincide with points R or S. If $m\widehat{RS} = 140$, what is the probability that $m\angle RCS = 70$?

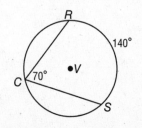

10-4 Word Problem Practice

Inscribed Angles

1. ARENA A circus arena is lit by five lights equally spaced around the perimeter.

What is $m\angle 1$?

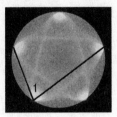

2. FIELD OF VIEW The figure shows a top view of two people in front of a very tall rectangular wall. The wall makes a chord of a circle that passes through both people.

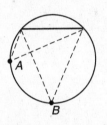

Which person has more of their horizontal field of vision blocked by the wall?

3. RHOMBI Paul is interested in circumscribing a circle around a rhombus that is not a square. He is having great difficulty doing so. Can you help him? Explain.

4. STREETS Three kilometers separate the intersections of Cross and Upton and Cross and Hope.

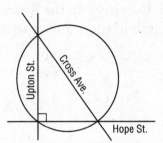

What is the distance between the intersection of Upton and Hope and the point midway between the intersections of Upton and Cross and Cross and Hope?

5. INSCRIBED HEXAGONS You will prove that the sum of the measures of alternate interior angles in an inscribed hexagon is 360.

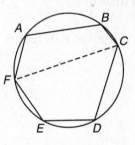

a. How are $\angle A$ and $\angle BCF$ related? Similarly, how are $\angle E$ and $\angle DCF$ related?

b. Show that $m\angle A + m\angle BCD + m\angle E = 360$.

Lesson 10-4

10-4 Enrichment

Formulas for Regular Polygons

Suppose a regular polygon of n sides is inscribed in a circle of radius r. The figure shows one of the isosceles triangles formed by joining the endpoints of one side of the polygon to the center C of the circle. In the figure, s is the length of each side of the regular polygon, and a is the length of the segment from C perpendicular to $\overline{AB}$.

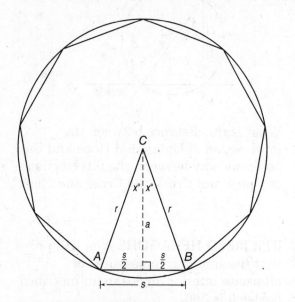

Use your knowledge of triangles and trigonometry to solve the following problems.

1. Find a formula for x in terms of the number of sides n of the polygon.

2. Find a formula for s in terms of n and r. Use trigonometry.

3. Find a formula for a in terms of n and r. Use trigonometry.

4. Find a formula for the *perimeter* of the regular polygon in terms of n and r.

10-5 Study Guide and Intervention

Tangents

Tangents A **tangent** to a circle intersects the circle in exactly one point, called the **point of tangency**. There are important relationships involving tangents. A **common tangent** is a line, ray, or segment that is tangent to two circles in the same plane.

- A line is tangent to a circle if and only if it is perpendicular to a radius at a point of tangency.
- If two segments from the same exterior point are tangent to a circle, then they are congruent.

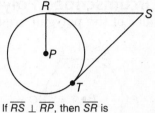

If $\overline{RS} \perp \overline{RP}$, then $\overline{SR}$ is tangent to $\odot P$. If $\overline{SR}$ is tangent to $\odot P$, then $\overline{RS} \perp \overline{RP}$. If $\overline{SR}$ and $\overline{ST}$ are tangent to $\odot P$, then $\overline{SR} \cong \overline{ST}$.

Example $\overline{AB}$ **is tangent to** $\odot C$. **Find** x.

AB is tangent to $\odot C$, so $\overline{AB}$ is perpendicular to radius $\overline{BC}$. $\overline{CD}$ is a radius, so $CD = 8$ and $AC = 9 + 8$ or 17. Use the Pythagorean Theorem with right $\triangle ABC$.

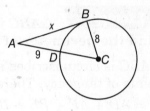

$$(AB)^2 + (BC)^2 = (AC)^2 \qquad \text{Pythagorean Theorem}$$
$$x^2 + 8^2 = 17^2 \qquad \text{Substitution}$$
$$x^2 + 64 = 289 \qquad \text{Simplify.}$$
$$x^2 = 225 \qquad \text{Subtract 64 from each side.}$$
$$x = 15 \qquad \text{Take the positive square root of each side.}$$

Exercises

Find x. **Assume that segments that appear to be tangent are tangent.**

1.
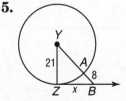

2.
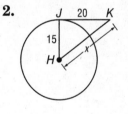

3.
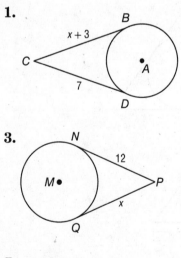

4.
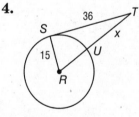

5.

6.
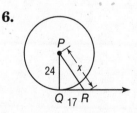

Glencoe Geometry

Lesson 10-5

10-5 Study Guide and Intervention *(continued)*

Tangents

Circumscribed Polygons When a polygon is circumscribed about a circle, all of the sides of the polygon are tangent to the circle.

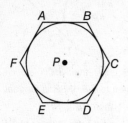

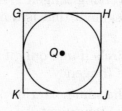

Hexagon *ABCDEF* is circumscribed about ⊙*P*.
$\overline{AB}, \overline{BC}, \overline{CD}, \overline{DE}, \overline{EF}$, and $\overline{FA}$ are tangent to ⊙*P*.

Square *GHJK* is circumscribed about ⊙*Q*.
$\overline{GH}, \overline{JH}, \overline{JK}$, and $\overline{KG}$ are tangent to ⊙*Q*.

Example △*ABC* is circumscribed about ⊙*O*.
Find the perimeter of △*ABC*.

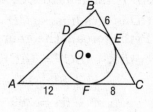

△*ABC* is circumscribed about ⊙*O*, so points *D*, *E*, and *F* are points of tangency. Therefore *AD* = *AF*, *BE* = *BD*, and *CF* = *CE*.

$P = AD + AF + BE + BD + CF + CE$

$= 12 + 12 + 6 + 6 + 8 + 8$

$= 52$

The perimeter is 52 units.

Exercises

For each figure, find *x*. Then find the perimeter.

1.
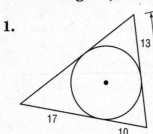

2.
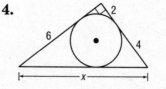

3.
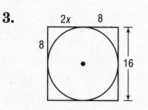

4.
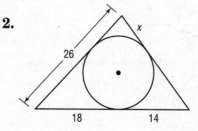

5.
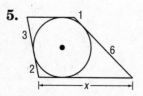

6.
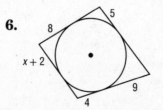

10-5 Skills Practice

Tangents

Determine whether each segment is tangent to the given circle.
Justify your answer.

1. $\overline{HI}$

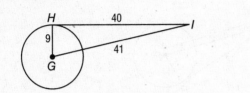

2. $\overline{AB}$

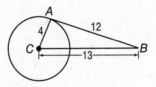

Find x. Assume that segments that appear to be tangent are tangent. Round to the nearest tenth if necessary.

3.

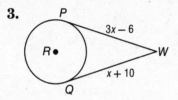

4.

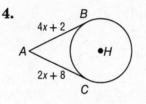

5.

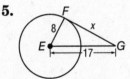

6.

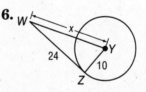

For each figure, find x. Then find the perimeter.

7.

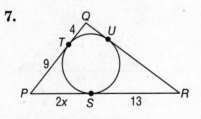

8.

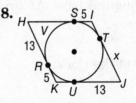

Lesson 10-5

10-5 Practice

Tangents

Determine whether each segment is tangent to the given circle. Justify your answer.

1. $\overline{MP}$

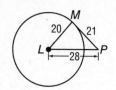

2. $\overline{QR}$

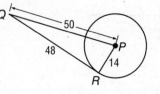

Find x. Assume that segments that appear to be tangent are tangent. Round to the nearest tenth if necessary.

3.

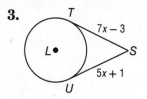

4.

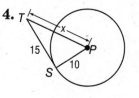

For each figure, find x. Then find the perimeter.

5.

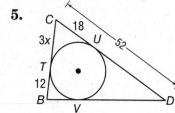

6.

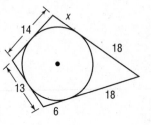

7. **CLOCKS** The design shown in the figure is that of a circular clock face inscribed in a triangular base. *AF* and *FC* are equal.

   a. Find *AB*.

   b. Find the perimeter of the clock.

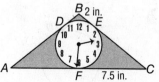

10-5 Word Problem Practice

Tangents

1. CANALS The concrete canal in Landtown is shaped like a "V" at the bottom. One day, Maureen accidentally dropped a cylindrical tube as she was walking and it rolled to the bottom of the dried out concrete canal. The figure shows a cross section of the tube at the bottom of the canal.

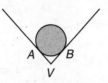

Compare the lengths AV and BV.

2. PACKAGING Taylor packed a sphere inside a cubic box. He had painted the sides of the box black before putting the sphere inside. When the sphere was later removed, he discovered that the black paint had not completely dried and there were black marks on the sides of the sphere at the points of tangency with the sides of the box. If the black marks are used as the vertices of a polygon, what kind of polygon results?

3. JEWELRY Juanita is designing a pendant with a circular gem inscribed in a triangle. Find the values of x, y, and z. Then find the perimeter of the triangle.

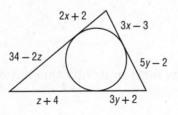

4. ROLLING A wheel is rolling down an incline. Twelve evenly spaced diameters form spokes of the wheel.

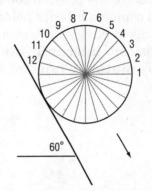

When spoke 2 is vertical, which spoke will be perpendicular to the incline?

5. DESIGN Amanda wants to make this design of circles inside an equilateral triangle.

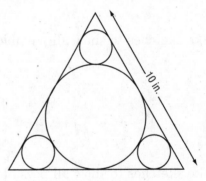

a. What is the radius of the large circle to the nearest hundredth of an inch?

b. What are the radii of the smaller circles to the nearest hundredth of an inch?

Lesson 10-5

10-5 Enrichment

Tangent Circles

Two circles in the same plane are **tangent circles** if they have exactly one point in common. Tangent circles with no common interior points are **externally tangent**. If tangent circles have common interior points, then they are **internally tangent**. Three or more circles are **mutually tangent** if each pair of them is tangent.

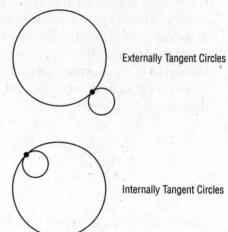

Externally Tangent Circles

Internally Tangent Circles

1. Make sketches to show all possible positions of three mutually tangent circles.

2. Make sketches to show all possible positions of four mutually tangent circles.

3. Make sketches to show all possible positions of five mutually tangent circles.

4. Write a conjecture about the number of possible positions for *n* mutually tangent circles if *n* is a whole number greater than four.

10-5 Graphing Calculator Activity

TI-Nspire: Exploring Tangents

A line that intersects a circle in exactly one point is called a **tangent** to the circle. You can use TI-Nspire to explore some of the characteristics of tangents. Use the following steps to draw two lines that are tangent to a circle.

Step 1 Draw a circle.

- From the **8: Shapes** menu select **1: Circle**.

- Place the cursor on the left center part of the screen and press ⊛. You have established the center of the circle.

- Press the left arrow to increase the radius length of the circle. Press ⊛ when the circle has a desirable radius.

- From the **1: Actions** menu select **5: Text**. Press ⊛ near the center of the circle and label the center of the circle C.

Step 2 Draw a tangent line.

- From the **6: Points and Lines** menu select **7: Tangent**.

- Move the cursor to the circle. Press ⊛. A tangent line is now drawn.

- Move the cursor to another point on the circle so that a new tangent line appears and intersects the first tangent line. Press ⊛.

- From the **1: Actions** menu use the **5: Text** function to label the first point of tangency T, the second point of tangency, S and the point where the two tangents intersect, A.

Exercises

Use the measuring capabilities of TI-Nspire to explore the characteristics of tangents.

1. Measure the lengths of $\overline{AT}$ and $\overline{AS}$.

2. Make a conjecture about AT and AS.

3. From the **6: Points and Lines** menu use the **5: Segment** tool to draw radii $\overline{CT}$ and $\overline{CS}$. Measure $\angle CTA$ and $\angle CSA$.

4. Make a conjecture about the angles formed by a radius and a tangent to a circle.

Lesson 10-5

10-5 Geometer's Sketchpad Activity

Exploring Tangents

A line that intersects a circle in exactly one point is called a **tangent** to the circle. You can use The Geometer's Sketchpad to explore some of the characteristics of tangents. Use the following steps to draw two lines that are tangent to a circle.

Step 1: Use the Compass tool to draw a circle. Choose the Compass tool in the Tool Box. Then move the pointer to the sketch plane, where it becomes a circle. Position the pointer anywhere on the sketch plane to locate the center of the circle. Then click and drag the pointer until the circle has the desired radius. Release the mouse button to complete the circle. Label the center of the circle A.

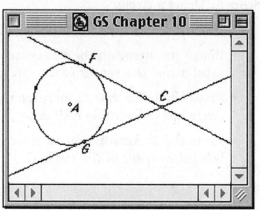

Step 2: Next, use the Point tool to draw a point outside the circle. Label the point C.

Step 3: Use the Line tool to draw a line through point C that intersects circle A in exactly one point. Label the point of intersection F.

Step 4: Repeat the procedure in Step 3 to draw another line through point C that is tangent to circle A at point G.

The lines drawn to the circle are tangents to the circle. *Note that these tangents are approximate, since it is difficult to find the exact point where the line touches the circle.*

Exercises

Use the measuring capabilities of The Geometer's Sketchpad to explore the characteristics of tangents.

1. Measure the lengths of $\overline{CF}$ and $\overline{CG}$.

2. Move point C closer to the circle. Adjust $\overline{CF}$ and $\overline{CG}$ accordingly. Make a conjecture about the measurements of $\overline{CF}$ and $\overline{CG}$.

3. Use the Segment tool to draw radii $\overline{AF}$ and $\overline{AG}$. Measure $\angle AFC$ and $\angle AGC$.

4. Make a conjecture about the angles formed by a radius and a tangent to a circle.

10-6 Study Guide and Intervention

Secants, Tangents, and Angle Measures

Intersections On or Inside a Circle A line that intersects a circle in exactly two points is called a **secant**. The measures of angles formed by secants and tangents are related to intercepted arcs.

- If two secants or chords intersect in the interior of a circle, then the measure of the angle formed is one half the sum of the measure of the arcs intercepted by the angle and its vertical angle.

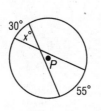

$$m\angle 1 = \tfrac{1}{2}(m\widehat{PR} + m\widehat{QS})$$

- If a secant (or chord) and a tangent intersect at the point of tangency, then the measure of each angle formed is one half the measure of its intercepted arc.

$$m\angle XTV = \tfrac{1}{2}\,m\widehat{TUV}$$
$$m\angle YTV = \tfrac{1}{2}\,m\widehat{TV}$$

Example 1 Find x.

The two chords intersect inside the circle, so x is equal to one half the sum of the measures of the arcs intercepted by the angle and its vertical angle.

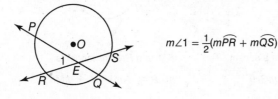

$$x = \tfrac{1}{2}(30 + 55)$$
$$= \tfrac{1}{2}(85)$$
$$= 42.5$$

Example 2 Find y.

The chord and the tangent intersect at the point of tangency, so the measure of the angle is one half the measure of its intercepted arc.

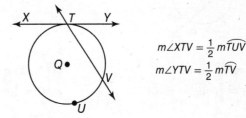

$$y = \tfrac{1}{2}(168)$$
$$= 84$$

Exercises

Find each measure. Assume that segments that appear to be tangent are tangent.

1. $m\angle 1$

2. $m\widehat{GH}$

3. $m\angle 3$

4. $m\widehat{RT}$

5. $m\angle 5$

6. $m\angle 6$

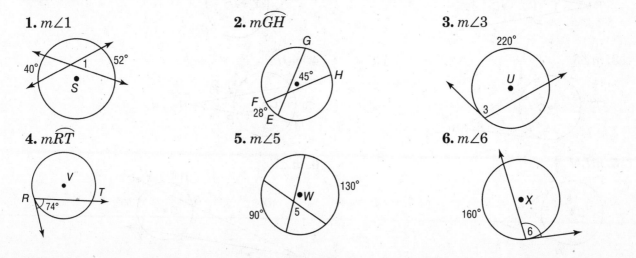

10-6 Study Guide and Intervention (continued)

Secants, Tangents, and Angle Measures

Intersections Outside a Circle If secants and tangents intersect outside a circle, they form an angle whose measure is related to the intercepted arcs.

If two secants, a secant and a tangent, or two tangents intersect in the exterior of a circle, then the measure of the angle formed is one half the difference of the measures of the intercepted arcs.

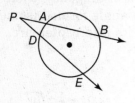

$\overrightarrow{PB}$ and $\overrightarrow{PE}$ are secants.

$m\angle P = \frac{1}{2}(m\widehat{BE} - m\widehat{AD})$

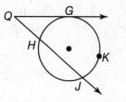

$\overrightarrow{QG}$ is a tangent. $\overrightarrow{QJ}$ is a secant.

$m\angle Q = \frac{1}{2}(m\widehat{GKJ} - m\widehat{GH})$

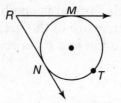

$\overrightarrow{RM}$ and $\overrightarrow{RN}$ are tangents.

$m\angle R = \frac{1}{2}(m\widehat{MTN} - m\widehat{MN})$

Example Find $m\angle MPN$.

$\angle MPN$ is formed by two secants that intersect in the exterior of a circle.

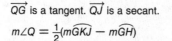

$m\angle MPN = \frac{1}{2}(m\widehat{MN} - m\widehat{RS})$

$= \frac{1}{2}(34 - 18)$

$= \frac{1}{2}(16)$ or 8

The measure of the angle is 8.

Exercises

Find each measure. Assume that segments that appear to be tangent are tangent.

1. $m\angle 1$

2. $m\angle 2$

3. $m\angle 3$

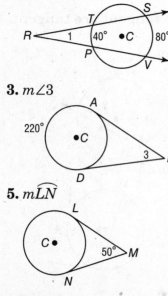

4. $m\widehat{JP}$

5. $m\widehat{LN}$

6. $m\angle V$

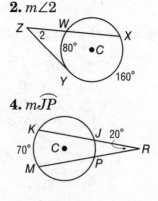

10-6 Skills Practice

Secants, Tangents, and Angle Measures

Find each measure. Assume that segment that appear to be tangent are tangent.

1. $m\angle 1$

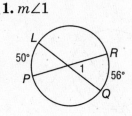

2. $m\angle 2$

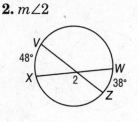

3. $m\angle 3$

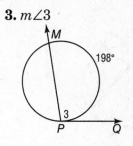

4. $m\angle 4$

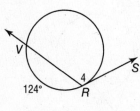

5. $m\angle 5$

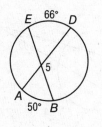

6. $m\angle 6$

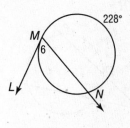

7. $m\angle R$

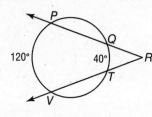

8. $m\angle K$

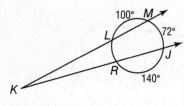

9. $m\angle U$

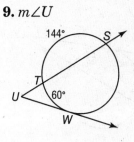

10. $m\angle S$

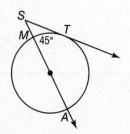

11. $m\widehat{DPA}$

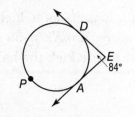

12. $m\widehat{LJ}$

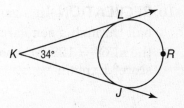

10-6 Practice

Secants, Tangents, and Angle Measures

Find each measure. Assume that any segments that appear to be tangent are tangent.

1. $m\angle 1$

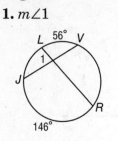

2. $m\angle 2$

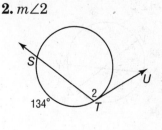

3. $m\angle 3$

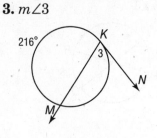

4. $m\angle R$

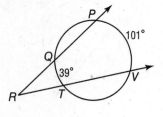

5. $m\widehat{GJ}$

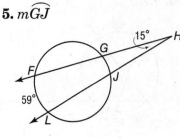

6. $m\angle R$

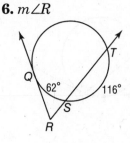

7. $m\angle Y$

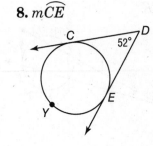

8. $m\widehat{CE}$

9. $m\widehat{YAB}$

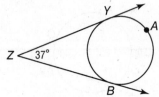

10. RECREATION In a game of kickball, Rickie has to kick the ball through a semicircular goal to score. If $m\widehat{XZ} = 58$ and the $m\widehat{XY} = 122$, at what angle must Rickie kick the ball to score? Explain.

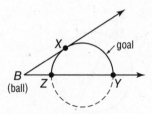

10-6 Word Problem Practice

Secants, Tangents, and Angle Measures

1. TELESCOPES Vanessa looked through her telescope at a mountainous landscape. The figure shows what she saw. Based on the view, approximately what angle does the side of the mountain that runs from A to B make with the horizontal?

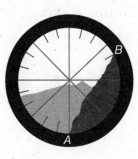

2. RADAR Two airplanes were tracked on radar. They followed the paths shown in the figure.

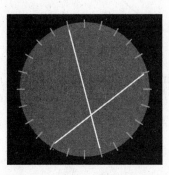

What is the acute angle between their flight paths?

3. EASELS Francisco is a painter. He places a circular canvas on his A-frame easel and carefully centers it. The apex of the easel is 30° and the measure of arc BC is 22°. What is the measure of arc AB?

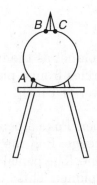

4. FLYING When flying at an altitude of 5 miles, the lines of sight to the horizon looking north and south make about a 173.7° angle. How much of the longitude line directly under the plane is visible from 5 miles high?

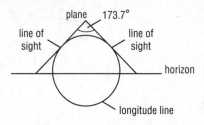

5. STAINED GLASS Pablo made the stained glass window shown. He used an inscribed square and equilateral triangle for the design.

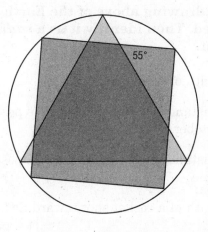

a. Label the angle measures on the outer edge of the triangle.

b. Label all of the arcs with their degree measure.

10-6 Enrichment

Orbiting Bodies

The path of the Earth's orbit around the sun is elliptical. However, it is often viewed as circular.

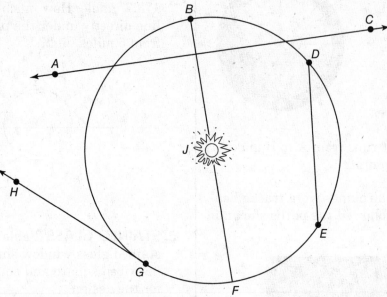

Use the drawing above of the Earth orbiting the sun to name the line or segment described. Then identify it as a *radius*, *diameter*, *chord*, *tangent*, or *secant* of the orbit.

1. the path of an asteroid

2. the distance between the Earth's position in July and the Earth's position in October

3. the distance between the Earth's position in December and the Earth's position in June

4. the path of a rocket shot toward Saturn

5. the path of a sunbeam

6. If a planet has a moon, the moon circles the planet as the planet circles the Sun. To visualize the path of the moon, cut two circles from a piece of cardboard, one with a diameter of 4 inches and one with a diameter of 1 inch.

Tape the larger circle firmly to a piece of paper. Poke a pencil point through the smaller circle, close to the edge. Roll the small circle around the outside of the large one. The pencil will trace out the path of a moon circling its planet. This kind of curve is called an epicycloid. To see the path of the planet around the Sun, poke the pencil through the center of the small circle (the planet), and roll the small circle around the large one (the Sun).

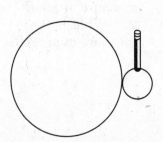

10-7 Study Guide and Intervention

Special Segments in a Circle

Segments Intersecting Inside a Circle If two chords intersect in a circle, then the products of the lengths of the chord segments are equal.

$$a \cdot b = c \cdot d$$

Example Find x.

The two chords intersect inside the circle, so the products $AB \cdot BC$ and $EB \cdot BD$ are equal.

$AB \cdot BC = EB \cdot BD$

$6 \cdot x = 8 \cdot 3$ Substitution

$6x = 24$ Multiply.

$x = 4$ Divide each side by 6.

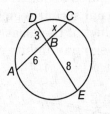

$$AB \cdot BC = EB \cdot BD$$

Exercises

Find x. Assume that segments that appear to be tangent are tangent. Round to the nearest tenth if necessary.

1.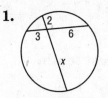

2.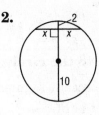

3.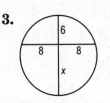

4.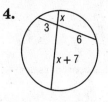

5.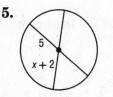

6.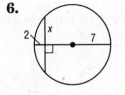

7.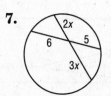

8.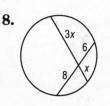

Lesson 10-7

10-7 Study Guide and Intervention (continued)

Special Segments in a Circle

Segments Intersecting Outside a Circle If secants and tangents intersect outside a circle, then two products are equal. A **secant segment** is a segment of a secant line that has exactly one endpoint on the circle. A secant segment that lies in the exterior of the circle is called an **external secant segment**. A **tangent segment** is a segment of a tangent with one endpoint on the circle.

- If two secants are drawn to a circle from an exterior point, then the product of the measures of one secant segment and its external secant segment is equal to the product of the measures of the other secant segment and its external secant segment.

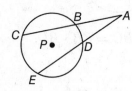

$\overline{AC}$ and $\overline{AE}$ are secant segments.

$\overline{AB}$ and $\overline{AD}$ are external secant segments.

$AC \cdot AB = AE \cdot AD$

- If a tangent segment and a secant segment are drawn to a circle from an exterior point, then the square of the measure of the tangent segment is equal to the product of the measures of the secant segment and its external secant segment.

$\overline{AB}$ is a tangent segment.

$\overline{AD}$ is a secant segment.

$\overline{AC}$ is an external secant segment.

$(AB)^2 = AD \cdot AC$

Example $\overline{AB}$ **is tangent to the circle. Find** x. **Round to the nearest tenth.**

The tangent segment is $\overline{AB}$, the secant segment is $\overline{BD}$, and the external secant segment is $\overline{BC}$.

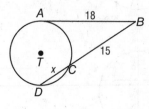

$(AB)^2 = BC \cdot BD$

$(18)^2 = 15(15 + x)$ Substitution.

$324 = 225 + 15x$ Multiply.

$99 = 15x$ Subtract 225 from both sides.

$6.6 = x$ Divide both sides by 15.

Exercises

Find x. **Round to the nearest tenth. Assume segments that appear to be tangent are tangent.**

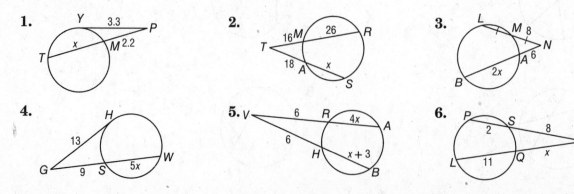

10-7 Skills Practice

Special Segments in a Circle

Find x to the nearest tenth if necessary. Assume that segments that appear to be tangent are tangent.

1.

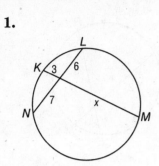

2.

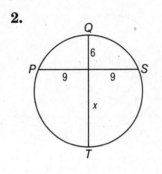

3.

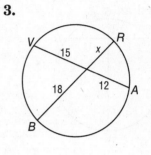

4.

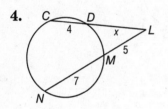

5.

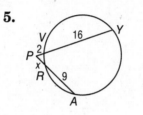

6.

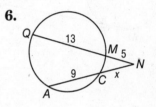

7.

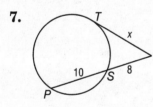

8.

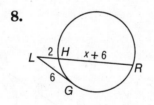

9.

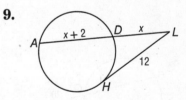

Lesson 10-7

10-7 Practice

Special Segments in a Circle

Find *x*. Assume that segments that appear to be tangent are tangent. Round to the nearest tenth if necessary

1.

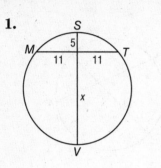

2.

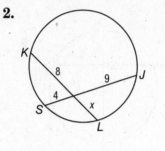

3.

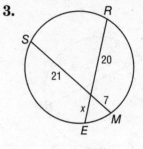

4.

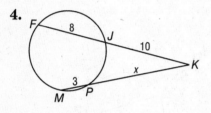

5.

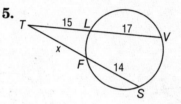

6.

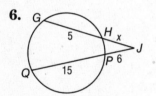

7.

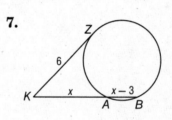

8.

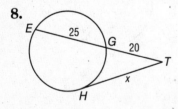

9.

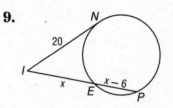

10. CONSTRUCTION An arch over an apartment entrance is 3 feet high and 9 feet wide. Find the radius of the circle containing the arc of the arch.

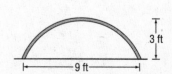

10-7 Word Problem Practice

Special Segments in a Circle

1. ICE SKATING Ted skated through one of the face-off circles at a skating rink. His path through the circle is shown in the figure. Given that the face-off circle is 15 feet in diameter, what distance within the face-off circle did Ted travel?

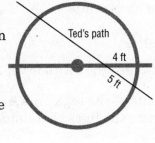

Ted's path
4 ft
5 ft

2. HORIZONS Assume that Earth is a perfect sphere with a diameter of 7926 miles. From an altitude of a miles, how long is the horizon line h?

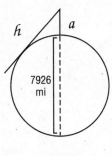

h a
7926 mi

3. AXLES The figure shows the cross-section of an axle held in place by a triangular sleeve. A brake extends from the apex of the triangle. When the brake is extended 2.5 inches into the sleeve, it comes into contact with the axle. What is the diameter of the axle?

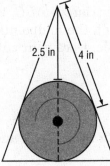

2.5 in   4 in

4. ARCHEOLOGY Scientists unearthed part of a circular wall. They made the measurements shown in the figure.

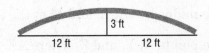

3 ft
12 ft   12 ft

Based on the information in the figure, what was the radius of the circle?

5. PIZZA DELIVERY Pizza Power is located at the intersection of Northern Boulevard and Highway 1 in a city with a circular highway running all the way around its outskirts. The radius of the circular highway is 13 miles. Pizza Power puts the map shown below on its take-out menus.

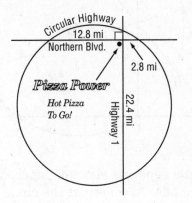

Circular Highway
12.8 mi
Northern Blvd.
2.8 mi
Pizza Power
Hot Pizza
To Go!
22.4 mi
Highway 1

a. How many miles away is the Circular Highway from Pizza Power if you travel north on Highway 1?

b. The city builds a new road along the diameter of Circular Highway that passes through the intersection of Northern Boulevard and Highway 1. Along this new road, about how many miles is it (the shorter way) to the Circular Highway from Pizza Power?

Lesson 10-7

10-7 Enrichment

The Nine-Point Circle

The figure below illustrates a surprising fact about triangles and circles. Given any $\triangle ABC$, there is a circle that contains all of the following nine points:

(1) the midpoints K, L, and M of the sides of $\triangle ABC$

(2) the points X, Y, and Z, where $\overline{AX}$, $\overline{BY}$, and $\overline{CZ}$ are the altitudes of $\triangle ABC$

(3) the points R, S, and T which are the midpoints of the segments $\overline{AH}$, $\overline{BH}$, and $\overline{CH}$ that join the vertices of $\triangle ABC$ to the point H where the lines containing the altitudes intersect.

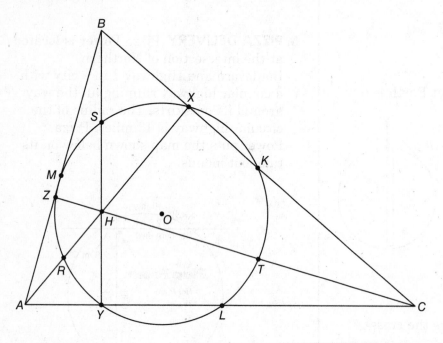

1. On a separate sheet of paper, draw an obtuse triangle ABC. Use your straightedge and compass to construct the circle passing through the midpoints of the sides. Be careful to make your construction as accurate as possible. Does your circle contain the other six points described above?

2. In the figure you constructed for Exercise 1, draw $\overline{RK}$, $\overline{SL}$, and $\overline{TM}$. What do you observe?

10-8 Study Guide and Intervention

Equations of Circles

Equation of a Circle A **circle** is the locus of points in a plane equidistant from a given point. You can use this definition to write an equation of a circle.

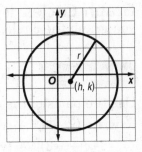

Standard Equation of a Circle	An equation for a circle with center at (h, k) and a radius of r units is $(x - h)^2 + (y - k)^2 = r^2$.

Example Write an equation for a circle with center $(-1, 3)$ and radius 6.

Use the formula $(x - h)^2 + (y - k)^2 = r^2$ with $h = -1$, $k = 3$, and $r = 6$.

$$(x - h)^2 + (y - k)^2 = r^2 \qquad \text{Equation of a circle}$$
$$(x - (-1))^2 + (y - 3)^2 = 6^2 \qquad \text{Substitution}$$
$$(x + 1)^2 + (y - 3)^2 = 36 \qquad \text{Simplify.}$$

Exercises

Write the equation of each circle.

1. center at $(0, 0)$, radius 8

2. center at $(-2, 3)$, radius 5

3. center at $(2, -4)$, radius 1

4. center at $(-1, -4)$, radius 2

5. center at $(-2, -6)$, diameter 8

6. center at origin, diameter 4

7. center at $(3, -4)$, passes through $(-1, -4)$

8. center at $(0, 3)$, passes through $(2, 0)$

9.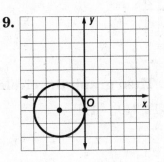

10.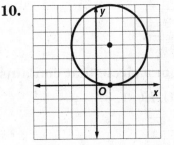

Lesson 10-8

10-8 Study Guide and Intervention *(continued)*

Equations of Circles

Graph Circles If you are given an equation of a circle, you can find information to help you graph the circle.

Example Graph $(x + 3)^2 + (y + 1)^2 = 9$.

Use the parts of the equation to find (h, k) and r.

Rewrite $(x + 3)^2 + (y - 1)^2 = 9$ to find the center and the radius.

$$[x - (-3)]^2 + (y - 1)^2 = 3^2$$
$$\uparrow \qquad \uparrow \quad \uparrow$$
$$(x - h)^2 + (y - k)^2 = r^2$$

So $h = -3$, $k = 1$, and $r = 3$. The center is at $(-3, 1)$ and the radius is 3.

Exercises

For each circle with the given equation, state the coordinates of the center and the measure of the radius. Then graph the equation.

1. $x^2 + y^2 = 16$

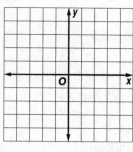
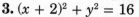

2. $(x - 2)^2 + (y - 1)^2 = 9$

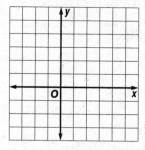

3. $(x + 2)^2 + y^2 = 16$

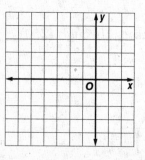

4. $x^2 + (y - 1)^2 = 9$

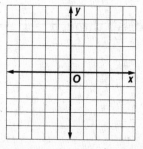

Write an equation of a circle that contains each set of points. Then graph the circle.

5. $F(-2, 2)$, $G(-1, 1)$, $H(-1, 3)$

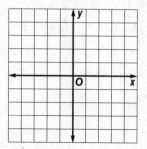

6. $R(-2, 1)$, $S(-4, -1)$, $T(0, -1)$

10-8 Skills Practice

Equations of Circles

Write the equation of each circle.

1. center at origin, radius 6

2. center at (0, 0), radius 2

3. center at (4, 3), radius 9

4. center at (7, 1), diameter 24

5. center at (−4, −1), passes through (−2, 3)

6. center at (5, −2), passes through (4, 0)

7.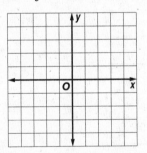

8.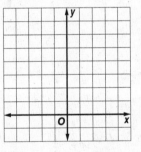

For each circle with the given equation, state the coordinates of the center and the measure of the radius. Then graph the equation.

9. $x^2 + y^2 = 16$

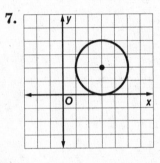

10. $(x - 1)^2 + (y - 4)^2 = 9$

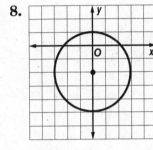

Write an equation of a circle that contains each set of points. Then graph the circle.

11. $A(-2, 3)$, $B(1, 0)$, $C(4, 3)$

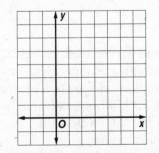

12. $F(3, 0)$, $G(5, -2)$, $H(1, -2)$

Lesson 10-8

10-8 Practice

Equations of Circles

Write the equation of each circle.

1. center at (0, 0), diameter 18

2. center at (−7, 11), radius 8

3. center at (−1, 8), passes through (9, 3)

4. center at (−3, −3), passes through (−2, 3)

For each circle with the given equation, state the coordinates of the center and the measure of the radius. Then graph the equation.

5. $x^2 + y^2 - 4 = 0$

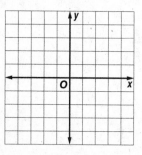

6. $x^2 + y^2 + 6x - 6y + 9 = 0$

Write an equation of a circle that contains each set of points. Then graph the circle.

7. $A(-2, 2)$, $B(2, -2)$, $C(6, 2)$

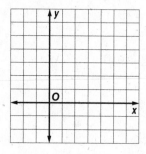

8. $R(5, 0)$, $S(-5, 0)$, $T(0, -5)$

Find the point(s) of intersection, if any, between each circle and line with the equations given.

9. $x^2 + y^2 = 25$; $y = x$

10. $(x + 4)^2 + (y - 3)^2 = 25$; $y = x + 2$

11. EARTHQUAKES When an earthquake strikes, it releases seismic waves that travel in concentric circles from the epicenter of the earthquake. Seismograph stations monitor seismic activity and record the intensity and duration of earthquakes. Suppose a station determines that the epicenter of an earthquake is located about 50 kilometers from the station. If the station is located at the origin, write an equation for the circle that represents one of the concentric circles of seismic waves of the earthquake.

10-8 Word Problem Practice

Equations of Circles

1. **DESIGN** Arthur wants to write the equation of a circle that is inscribed in the square shown in the graph.

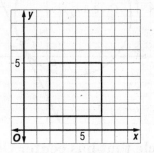

   What is the equation of the desired circle?

2. **DRAFTING** The design for a park is drawn on a coordinate graph. The perimeter of the park is modeled by the equation $(x - 3)^2 + (x - 7)^2 = 225$. Each unit on the graph represents 10 feet. What is the radius of the actual park?

3. **WALLPAPER** The design of a piece of wallpaper consists of circles that can be modeled by the equation $(x - a)^2 + (y - b)^2 = 4$, for all even integers b. Sketch part of the wallpaper on a grid.

4. **SECURITY RING** A circular safety ring surrounds a top-secret laboratory. On one map of the laboratory grounds, the safety ring is given by the equation $(x - 8)^2 + (y + 2)^2 = 324$. Each unit on the map represents 1 mile. What is the radius of the safety ring?

5. **DISTANCE** Cleo lives the same distance from the library, the post office, and her school. The table below gives the coordinates of these places on a map with a coordinate grid where one unit represents one yard.

Location	Coordinates
Library	(–78, 202)
Post Office	(111, 193)
School	(202, –106)

a. What are the coordinates of Cleo's home? Sketch the circle on a map locating all three places and Cleo's home.

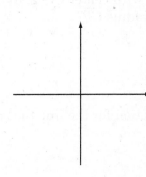

b. How far is Cleo's house from the places mentioned?

c. Write an equation for the circle that passes through the library, post office, and school.

Lesson 10-8

10-8   Enrichment

Equations of Circles and Tangents

Recall that the circle whose radius is r and whose center has coordinates (h, k) is the graph of $(x - h)^2 + (y - k)^2 = r^2$. You can use this idea and what you know about circles and tangents to find an equation of the circle that has a given center and is tangent to a given line.

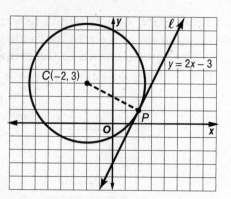

Use the following steps to find an equation for the circle that has center $C(-2, 3)$ and is tangent to the graph of $y = 2x - 3$. Refer to the figure.

1. State the slope of the line ℓ that has equation $y = 2x - 3$.

2. Suppose $\odot C$ with center $C(-2, 3)$ is tangent to line ℓ at point P. What is the slope of radius $\overline{CP}$?

3. Find an equation for the line that contains $\overline{CP}$.

4. Use your equation from Exercise 3 and the equation $y = 2x - 3$. At what point do the lines for these equations intersect? What are its coordinates?

5. Find the measure of radius $\overline{CP}$.

6. Use the coordinate pair $C(-2, 3)$ and your answer for Exercise 5 to write an equation for $\odot C$.

10 Student Recording Sheet

Use this recording sheet with pages 758–759 of the Student Edition.

Multiple Choice

Read each question. Then fill in the correct answer.

1. Ⓐ Ⓑ Ⓒ Ⓓ   3. Ⓐ Ⓑ Ⓒ Ⓓ   5. Ⓐ Ⓑ Ⓒ Ⓓ

2. Ⓕ Ⓖ Ⓗ Ⓙ   4. Ⓕ Ⓖ Ⓗ Ⓙ   6. Ⓕ Ⓖ Ⓗ Ⓙ

Short Response/Gridded Response

Record your answer in the blank.

For gridded response questions, also enter your answer in the grid by writing each number or symbol in a box. Then fill in the corresponding circle for that number or symbol.

7. _____

8. _____ *(grid in)*

9. _____

10. _____ *(grid in)*

11. _____

12. _____

8.

10.

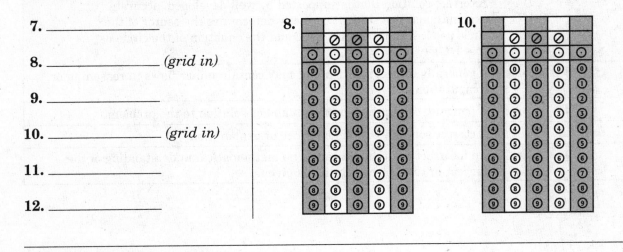

Extended Response

Record your answers for Question 13 on the back of this paper.

Assessment

10 Rubric for Scoring Extended-Response

General Scoring Guidelines

- If a student gives only a correct numerical answer to a problem but does not show how he or she arrived at the answer, the student will be awarded only 1 credit. All extended-response questions require the student to show work.

- A fully correct answer for a multiple-part question requires correct responses for all parts of the question. For example, if a question has three parts, the correct response to one or two parts of the question that required work to be shown is *not* considered a fully correct response.

- Students who use trial and error to solve a problem must show their method. Merely showing that the answer checks or is correct is not considered a complete response for full credit.

Exercise 13 Rubric

Score	Specific Criteria
4	A correct solution that is supported by well-developed, accurate explanations. The student correctly determines the center of the circle as $(1, -3)$, the radius as 3, and the equation of the circle as $(x - 1)^2 + (y + 3)^2 = 3^2$.
3	A generally correct solution, but may contain minor flaws in reasoning or computation.
2	A partially correct interpretation and/or solution to the problem.
1	A correct solution with no evidence or explanation.
0	An incorrect solution indicating no mathematical understanding of the concept or task, or no solution is given.

10 Chapter 10 Quiz 1

SCORE _____

(Lessons 10-1 and 10-2)

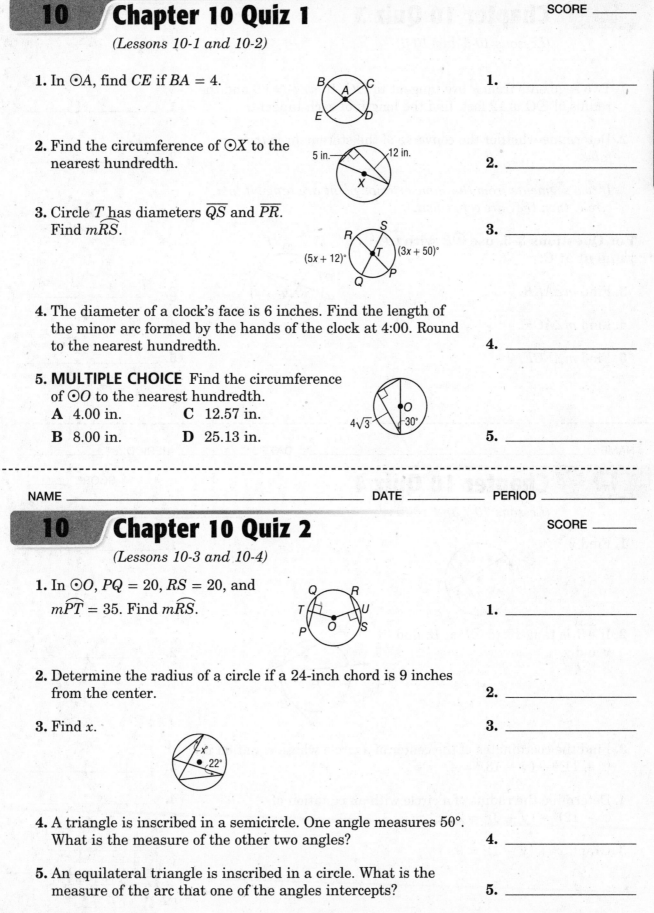

1. In ⊙*A*, find *CE* if *BA* = 4.

1. _____

2. Find the circumference of ⊙*X* to the nearest hundredth.

5 in. 12 in.

2. _____

3. Circle *T* has diameters $\overline{QS}$ and $\overline{PR}$. Find $m\widehat{RS}$.

$(5x + 12)°$ $(3x + 50)°$

3. _____

4. The diameter of a clock's face is 6 inches. Find the length of the minor arc formed by the hands of the clock at 4:00. Round to the nearest hundredth.

4. _____

5. **MULTIPLE CHOICE** Find the circumference of ⊙*O* to the nearest hundredth.

  A 4.00 in.   **C** 12.57 in.
  B 8.00 in.   **D** 25.13 in.

$4\sqrt{3}$ 30°

5. _____

10 Chapter 10 Quiz 2

SCORE _____

(Lessons 10-3 and 10-4)

1. In ⊙*O*, *PQ* = 20, *RS* = 20, and $m\widehat{PT} = 35$. Find $m\widehat{RS}$.

1. _____

2. Determine the radius of a circle if a 24-inch chord is 9 inches from the center.

2. _____

3. Find *x*.

x° 22°

3. _____

4. A triangle is inscribed in a semicircle. One angle measures 50°. What is the measure of the other two angles?

4. _____

5. An equilateral triangle is inscribed in a circle. What is the measure of the arc that one of the angles intercepts?

5. _____

NAME ______________________ DATE ____________ PERIOD ____________

10 Chapter 10 Quiz 3

SCORE ________

(Lessons 10-5 and 10-6)

1. Two segments from P are tangent to $\odot O$. If $m\angle P = 60$ and the radius of $\odot O$ is 12 feet, find the length of each tangent. **1.** ____________

2. Determine whether the converse of the statement is *true* or *false*. **2.** ____________

If two segments from the same exterior point are tangent to a circle, then they are congruent.

For Questions 3–5, use $\odot E$ with $\overleftrightarrow{CF}$ tangent at C.

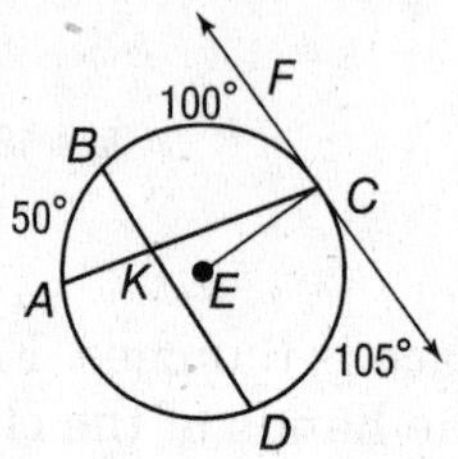

3. Find $m\angle AKB$. **3.** ____________

4. Find $m\angle ACF$. **4.** ____________

5. Find $m\angle ECF$. **5.** ____________

NAME ______________________ DATE ____________ PERIOD ____________

10 Chapter 10 Quiz 4

SCORE ________

(Lessons 10-7 and 10-8)

1. Find x. **1.** ____________

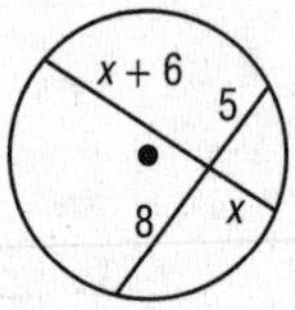

2. If $\overrightarrow{AB}$ is tangent to $\odot P$ at B, find x and y. **2.** ____________

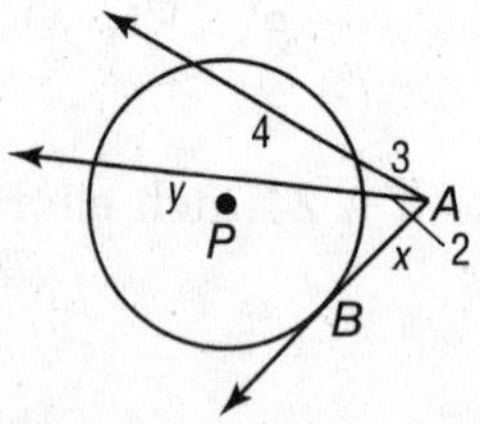

3. Find the coordinates of the center of a circle whose equation is $(x + 11)^2 + (y - 13)^2 = 4$. **3.** ____________

4. Determine the radius of a circle with an equation of $(x + 12)^2 + (y + 3)^2 = 225$. **4.** ____________

5. Graph $x^2 + (y - 1)^2 = 9$. **5.**

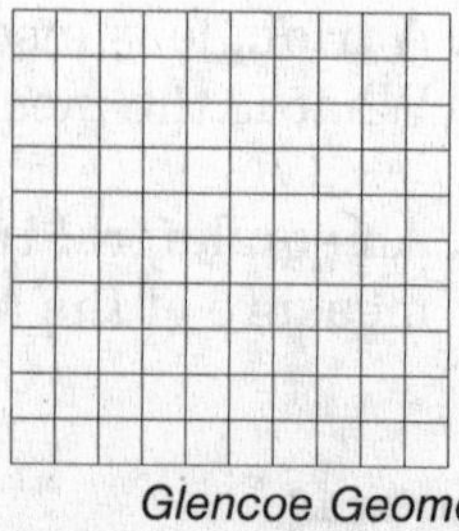

10 Chapter 10 Mid-Chapter Test

SCORE _____

(*Lessons 10-1 through 10-4*)

Part I *Write the letter for the correct answer in the blank at the right of each question.*

1. What is the name of the longest chord in a circle?

A diameter **B** radius **C** secant **D** tangent

1. _____

2. The radius of $\odot B$ is 4 centimeters and the circumference of $\odot A$ is 20π centimeters. Find *CD*.

F 10 cm **H** 24 cm

G 14 cm **J** 28 cm

2. _____

3. A chord of $\odot P$ measures 8 inches and the distance from the center to the chord is 3 inches. Find the radius of $\odot P$.

A 3 in. **B** 5 in. **C** $\sqrt{73}$ in. **D** 10 in.

3. _____

4. If $m\angle MON = 86$, find $m\angle MPN$.

F 86 **H** 43

G 45 **J** 30

4. _____

5. Find *x* if $m\angle 1 = 2x + 10$ and $m\angle 2 = 3x - 6$.

A 4 **C** 24

B 16 **D** 42

5. _____

Part II

6. $\overline{AE}$ is a diameter of $\odot G$ and $m\angle BGE = 136$. Find $m\widehat{AB}$.

6. _____

7. A circle with a radius of 12 inches has an arc that measures 8π inches. Find the measure of the central angle determined by this arc.

7. _____

8. In $\odot P$, chord $\overline{AB}$ measures $4x - 6$ centimeters and chord $\overline{CD}$ measures $6x - 12$ centimeters. If $\overline{AB}$ and $\overline{CD}$ are each 4 centimeters from *P*, find *AP*.

8. _____

9. A 15-inch by 8-inch tablecloth is placed on a circular table. Each of the four corners of the tablecloth touch the edge of the table. Determine the radius of the table.

9. _____

10. Quadrilateral *ABCD* is inscribed in $\odot P$. Find $m\angle ABC$.

10. _____

10 Chapter 10 Vocabulary Test

adjacent arcs	compound locus	minor arc
arc	concentric circles	pi (π)
center	congruent arcs	point of tangency
central angle	congruent circles	radius
chord	diameter	secant
chord segment	exterior segment	secant segment
circle	inscribed	semicircle
circumference	inscribed angle	tangent
circumscribed	intercepted arc	
common tangent	major arc	

Write whether each sentence is *true* or *false*. If false, replace the underlined word or phrase to make a true sentence.

1. The vertex of a <u>central</u> angle lies on the circle.

1. _____

2. A <u>circle</u> is the locus of all points in a plane equidistant from a given point.

2. _____

3. $C = 2\pi r$ is the formula for the <u>circumference</u> of a circle.

3. _____

4. The <u>diameter</u> of a circle is a segment with one endpoint at the center and the other endpoint on the circle.

4. _____

5. A <u>major arc</u> has measure greater than 0 but less than 180.

5. _____

Choose the correct word to complete each sentence.

6. The point of tangency is the point where a (*secant*, *tangent*) intersects a circle.

6. _____

7. A (*secant*, *chord*) is a line that intersects a circle in two points.

7. _____

Choose from the terms above to complete each sentence.

8. A(n) _____ is a line that intersects a circle in one point.

8. _____

9. A(n) _____ is an arc that measures 180°.

9. _____

10. _____ is an irrational number equal to the ratio of the circumference to the diameter of a circle.

10. _____

Define each term in your own words.

11. congruent arcs

11. _____

12. circumscribed polygon

12. _____

10 Chapter 10 Test, Form 1

SCORE _____

Write the letter for the correct answer in the blank at the right of each question.

For Questions 1–3, use ⊙X

1. Name a radius.

  A $\overline{XB}$ **B** $\overline{AB}$ **C** $\overline{BC}$ **D** $\overleftrightarrow{AC}$ 1. _____

2. Name a chord.

  F $\overline{XB}$ **G** $\overline{XC}$ **H** $\overline{BC}$ **D** $\overleftrightarrow{AC}$ 2. _____

3. Name a tangent.

  A $\overline{AB}$ **B** $\overline{BC}$ **C** $\overleftrightarrow{AC}$ **D** $\overleftrightarrow{BD}$ 3. _____

4. The wheels on Elliot's truck each have a circumference of 22 inches. Determine the radius of each wheel to the nearest lenth.

  F 2.5 in.   **G** 3.5 in.   **H** 5 in.   **J** 7 in.   4. _____

5. In ⊙C, $m\overarc{AB} = 72$. Find $m\angle BCD$.

  A 72   **C** 144

  B 108   **D** 180   5. _____

6. Find the length of $\overarc{PQ}$ in ⊙R to the nearest hundredth.

  F 9.42 m   **H** 3.14 m

  G 4.71 m   **J** 1.57 m   6. _____

7. In ⊙O, $AB = 12$ cm, $OE = 4$ cm, and $OF = 4$ cm. Find CF.

  A 6 cm   **C** 12 cm

  B 8 cm   **D** 24 cm   7. _____

8. Find the radius of a circle if a 48-meter chord is 7 meters from the center.

  F 14 m   **G** 24 m   **H** 25 m   **J** 41 m   8. _____

9. Find $m\angle ABC$.

  A 50   **C** 90

  B 70   **D** 140   9. _____

10. If $m\angle X = 126$, find $m\angle Z$.

  F 54   **H** 90

  G 63   **J** 126   10. _____

11. If $\overline{MN}$, $\overline{NO}$, and $\overline{MO}$ are tangent to ⊙P, find x.

  A 2 m   **C** 6 m

  B 5 m   **D** 8 m   11. _____

12. Find x.
   F 122   **H** 68
   G 95   **J** 61

12. _____

13. Find $m\widehat{VY}$.
   A 16   **C** 80
   B 56   **D** 112

13. _____

14. Find $m\widehat{LN}$.
   F 38   **H** 58
   G 56   **J** 76

14. _____

15. Find $m\angle H$.
   A 132   **C** 66
   B 68   **D** 34

15. _____

16. Find y.
   F 18   **H** 6
   G 12   **J** 4.5

16. _____

17. Find AF.
   A 11.25   **C** 7.5
   B 10   **D** 4

17. _____

18. Find the length of the radius of the circle whose equation is
$(x + 3)^2 + (y - 7)^2 = 289$.
   F 7   **G** 17   **H** 34   **J** 289

18. _____

19. Find the equation of a circle with center $(0, 0)$ and radius 4.
   A $x^2 + y^2 = 4$ **C** $(x - 4)^2 + (y - 4)^2 = 16$
   B $x^2 + y^2 = 16$ **D** $4x + 4y = 16$

19. _____

20. Identify the graph of $(x - 3)^2 + (y + 2)^2 = 4$.
   F   **G**   **H**   **J**

20. _____

Bonus Find x.

B: _____

10 Chapter 10 Test, Form 2A

SCORE _____

Write the letter for the correct answer in the blank at the right of each question.

For Questions 1–3, use ⊙O

1. Name a diameter.

  A $\overline{FG}$ **C** $\overrightarrow{AB}$

  B $\overline{AB}$ **D** $\overleftrightarrow{CE}$ **1.** _____

2. Name a chord.

  F $\overline{FO}$ **G** $\overline{AB}$ **H** $\overleftrightarrow{AB}$ **J** $\overleftrightarrow{CE}$ **2.** _____

3. Name a secant.

  A $\overline{FO}$ **B** $\overline{AB}$ **C** $\overrightarrow{AB}$ **D** $\overleftrightarrow{CE}$ **3.** _____

4. The diameter of a circular swimming pool is 15 feet. Find the circumference to the nearest hundredth.

  F 47.12 ft   **G** 63.81 ft   **H** 75.96 ft   **J** 94.24 ft   **4.** _____

5. In ⊙A, $m\angle BAD = 110$. Find $m\widehat{DE}$.

  A 35   **C** 70

  B 55   **D** 110   **5.** _____

6. Points X and Y lie on ⊙P so that $PX = 5$ meters and $m\angle XPY = 90$. Find the length of $\widehat{XY}$ to the nearest hundredth.

  F 3.93 m   **G** 7.85 m   **H** 15.71 m   **J** 19.63 m   **6.** _____

7. Chords $\overline{XY}$ and $\overline{WV}$ are equidistant from the center of ⊙O. If $XY = 2x + 30$ and $WV = 5x - 12$, find x.

  A 58   **B** 28   **C** 14   **D** 6   **7.** _____

8. Find the radius of ⊙O if $DE = 12$ inches and $\overline{DE}$ bisects $\overline{OF}$.

  F $2\sqrt{3}$ in.   **H** 8 in.

  G 6 in.   **J** $4\sqrt{3}$ in.   **8.** _____

9. Find x.

  A 122   **C** 58

  B 61   **D** 29   **9.** _____

10. $EFGH$ is a quadrilateral inscribed in ⊙P with $m\angle E = 72$ and $m\angle F = 49$. Find $m\angle H$.

  F 131   **G** 108   **H** 90   **J** 57   **10.** _____

11. If $\overline{AB}$ is tangent to ⊙C at A, find BC.

  A 6 in.   **C** $12\sqrt{3}$ in.

  B $4\sqrt{3}$ in.   **D** 24 in.   **11.** _____

12. $\overline{PQ}$, $\overline{QR}$, $\overline{RS}$, and $\overline{SP}$ are tangent to $\odot X$. Find RS.

    F 9 in.   **H** 13 in.

    G 12 in.   **J** cannot tell

12. _____

13. Circle A has its center at $A(3, 2)$, and $\overleftrightarrow{CB}$ is tangent to $\odot A$ at $B(6, 4)$. Find the slope of $\overleftrightarrow{CB}$.

    A 1   **B** $\frac{1}{2}$ **C** $-\frac{3}{2}$ **D** $-\frac{1}{2}$

13. _____

14. Find x.

    F 78   **H** 102

    G 90   **J** 156

14. _____

15. Find $m\widehat{AP}$.

    A 66   **C** 45

    B 57   **D** 21

15. _____

16. Find z.

    F 2   **H** 7

    G 4.5   **J** 8

16. _____

17. Find ZC.

    A 4   **C** 22

    B 16   **D** 32

17. _____

18. Find the center of the circle whose equation is $(x + 11)^2 + (y - 7)^2 = 121$.

    F $(-11, 7)$ **G** $(11, -7)$ **H** $(121, 49)$ **J** 11

18. _____

19. Find the equation of a circle whose center is at $(2, 3)$ and radius is 6.

    A $(x + 2)^2 + (y + 3)^2 = 6$ **C** $(x + 2)^2 + (y + 3)^2 = 36$

    B $(x - 2)^2 + (y - 3)^2 = 6$ **D** $(x - 2)^2 + (y - 3)^2 = 36$

19. _____

20. Find the equation of $\odot P$.

    F $x^2 + (y - 3)^2 = 4$ **H** $(x - 3)^2 + y^2 = 2$

    G $x^2 + (y - 3)^2 = 2$ **J** $(x - 3)^2 + y^2 = 4$

20. _____

Bonus A chord of the circle whose equation is $x^2 + y^2 = 57$ is tangent to the circle whose equation is $x^2 + y^2 = 32$ at the point $(4, -4)$. Find the length of the chord.

    B: _____

10 Chapter 10 Test, Form 2B

SCORE _____

Assessment

Write the letter for the correct answer in the blank at the right of each question.

For Questions 1–3, use ⊙D.

1. Name a radius.

  A $\overline{AB}$ **C** $\overline{CB}$

  B $\overline{DB}$ **D** $\overleftrightarrow{CE}$ **1.** _____

2. Name a chord that is not a diameter.

  F $\overline{AB}$ **G** $\overline{DB}$ **H** $\overline{CB}$ **J** $\overline{CE}$ **2.** _____

3. Name a secant.

  A $\overline{AB}$ **B** $\overline{DB}$ **C** $\overleftrightarrow{CB}$ **D** $\overleftrightarrow{CE}$ **3.** _____

4. The circumference of a steering wheel of a car is 20π inches. What is the radius of the steering wheel?

  F 10 in.   **G** 20 in.   **H** 40 in.   **J** 100 in.   **4.** _____

5. Find $m\overset{\frown}{GH}$.

  A 20°   **C** 70°

  B 50°   **D** 90°   **5.** _____

6. Points G and H lie on ⊙T so that $TH = 8$ meters and $m\angle GTH = 45$. Find the length of $\overset{\frown}{GH}$ to the nearest hundredth.

  F 6.28 m   **G** 12.57 m   **H** 25.13 m   **J** 37.70 m   **6.** _____

7. In ⊙X, chords $\overline{AB}$ and $\overline{CD}$ are congruent and $\overline{AB}$ is 9 units from X. Find the distance from $\overline{CD}$ to X.

  A 4.5 units   **B** 9 units   **C** 18 units   **D** cannot tell   **7.** _____

8. Determine AB.

  F $4\sqrt{2}$ units   **H** $8\sqrt{3}$ units

  G 8 units   **J** $4\sqrt{2} + 4$ units   **8.** _____

9. Find x.

  A 36   **C** 144

  B 72   **D** 180   **9.** _____

10. Triangle JKL is inscribed in ⊙P with diameter $\overline{JK}$ and $m\overset{\frown}{JL} = 130$. Find $m\angle KJL$.

  F 25°   **G** 50°   **H** 65°   **J** 130°   **10.** _____

11. The measure of an angle formed by two tangents to a circle is 90. If the radius of the circle is 8 centimeters, how far is the vertex of the angle from the center of the circle?

  A 8 cm   **B** $8\sqrt{2}$ cm   **C** $8\sqrt{3}$ cm   **D** 16 cm   **11.** _____

10 **Chapter 10 Test, Form 2B** *(continued)*

12. If $\overline{DE}$, $\overline{EF}$, and $\overline{FD}$ are tangent to $\odot A$, find EF.

    F 9 ft   **H** 7 ft

    G 8 ft   **J** 6 ft   **12.** ____

13. Circle A has its center at $A(5, 7)$ and $\overleftrightarrow{CB}$ is tangent to $\odot A$ at $B(2, 8)$. Find the slope of $\overleftrightarrow{CB}$.

    A 3   **B** $\frac{1}{3}$ **C** $-\frac{1}{3}$ **D** -3 **13.** ____

14. If $\overleftrightarrow{AB}$ is tangent to $\odot P$ at B, find $m\angle 1$.

    F 43°   **H** 137°

    G 86°   **J** 274°   **14.** ____

15. Find $m\angle PQR$ if $\overrightarrow{QP}$ and $\overrightarrow{QR}$ are tangent to $\odot X$.

    A 70°   **C** 125°

    B 110°   **D** 140°   **15.** ____

16. Find x.

    F $\frac{15}{7}$ **H** 9

    G 5   **J** $\frac{35}{3}$ **16.** ____

17. Find DE.

    A 7   **C** $\frac{59}{5}$

    B $\frac{48}{5}$ **D** $\frac{288}{25}$ **17.** ____

18. Find the center of the circle whose equation is $(x + 15)^2 + (y - 20)^2 = 100$.

    F $(-15, -20)$ **G** $(15, -20)$ **H** $(15, 20)$ **J** $(-15, 20)$ **18.** ____

19. Find the equation of a circle whose center is at $(-1, 5)$ and radius is 8.

    A $(x - 1)^2 + (y + 5)^2 = 8$ **C** $(x + 1)^2 + (y - 5)^2 = 8$

    B $(x - 1)^2 + (y + 5)^2 = 64$ **D** $(x + 1)^2 + (y - 5)^2 = 64$ **19.** ____

20. Find the equation of $\odot P$.

    F $(x + 4)^2 + (y - 2)^2 = 3$

    G $(x + 4)^2 + (y - 2)^2 = 9$

    H $(x - 4)^2 + (y + 2)^2 = 3$

    J $(x - 4)^2 + (y + 2)^2 = 9$ **20.** ____

Bonus Is the point $(-3, -5)$ inside, outside, or on the circle whose equation is $(x + 7)^2 + (y - 2)^2 = 62$?   **B:** _____

SCORE _____

10 Chapter 10 Test, Form 2C

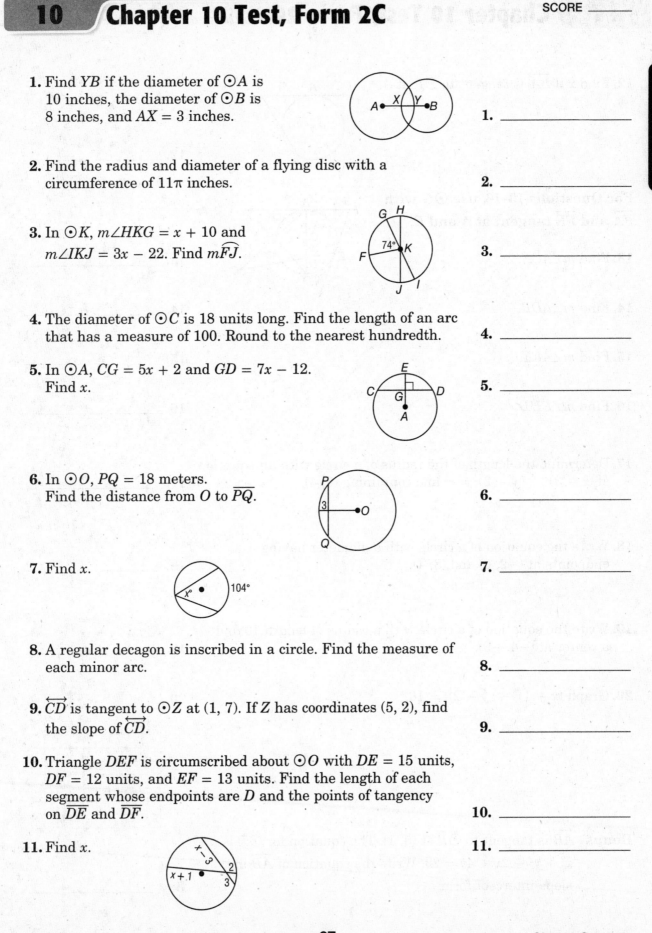

1. Find *YB* if the diameter of ⊙*A* is 10 inches, the diameter of ⊙*B* is 8 inches, and *AX* = 3 inches.

1. _____

2. Find the radius and diameter of a flying disc with a circumference of 11π inches.

2. _____

3. In ⊙*K*, m∠*HKG* = *x* + 10 and m∠*IKJ* = 3*x* − 22. Find m$\widehat{FJ}$.

3. _____

4. The diameter of ⊙*C* is 18 units long. Find the length of an arc that has a measure of 100. Round to the nearest hundredth.

4. _____

5. In ⊙*A*, *CG* = 5*x* + 2 and *GD* = 7*x* − 12. Find *x*.

5. _____

6. In ⊙*O*, *PQ* = 18 meters. Find the distance from *O* to $\overline{PQ}$.

6. _____

7. Find *x*.

7. _____

8. A regular decagon is inscribed in a circle. Find the measure of each minor arc.

8. _____

9. $\overleftrightarrow{CD}$ is tangent to ⊙*Z* at (1, 7). If *Z* has coordinates (5, 2), find the slope of $\overleftrightarrow{CD}$.

9. _____

10. Triangle *DEF* is circumscribed about ⊙*O* with *DE* = 15 units, *DF* = 12 units, and *EF* = 13 units. Find the length of each segment whose endpoints are *D* and the points of tangency on $\overline{DE}$ and $\overline{DF}$.

10. _____

11. Find *x*.

11. _____

12. Find x if $\overrightarrow{BA}$ is tangent to $\odot P$ at A.

12._____

For Questions 13–16, use $\odot G$ with $\overrightarrow{FA}$ and $\overrightarrow{FE}$ tangent at A and E.

13. Find $m\angle ACE$.

13._____

14. Find $m\angle ADB$.

14._____

15. Find $m\angle AFE$.

15._____

16. Find $m\angle EHD$.

16._____

17. Determine the length of the radius of a circle with an equation of $(x - 3)^2 + (y - 2)^2 = r^2$ and containing $(1, 4)$.

17._____

18. Write the equation of a circle with a diameter having endpoints at $(-2, 6)$ and $(8, 4)$.

18._____

19. Write the equation of a circle with a radius of length 10 and a center at $(-4, -9)$.

19._____

20. Graph $(x + 1)^2 + (y - 2)^2 = 16$.

20.

Bonus $\overleftrightarrow{AB}$ is tangent to $\odot P$ at $(5, 1)$. The equation for $\odot P$ is $x^2 + y^2 - 2x + 4y = 20$. Write the equation of $\overleftrightarrow{AB}$ in slope-intercept form.

B: _____

10 Chapter 10 Test, Form 2D

1. Find AB.

1. _____

2. Jon wants to put a circular decorative glass in a table. He cuts a hole in the table that is 20 inches in diameter. He uses a thin metal frame along the edge of the hole. What is the length of the frame?

2. _____

3. In $\odot L$, $m\angle QLN = 2x - 5$. Find x.

3. _____

4. The radius of $\odot C$ is 16 units long. Find the length of an arc that has a measure of 270. Round to the nearest hundredth.

4. _____

5. If $\overline{DE}$ bisects $\overline{AB}$, what is the measure of $\angle BCE$?

5. _____

6. Find the radius of $\odot O$ if $XY = 10$.

6. _____

7. Find x.

7. _____

8. Regular nonagon $ABCDEFGHI$ is inscribed in a circle. Find $m\widehat{AC}$.

8. _____

9. $\overleftrightarrow{EF}$ is tangent to circle P at $G(3, 6)$. If the slope of $\overleftrightarrow{EF}$ is $\frac{5}{3}$, what is the slope of $\overline{GP}$?

9. _____

10. Triangle GHI is circumscribed about $\odot K$ with $GH = 20$ units, $HI = 14$ units, and $IG = 12$ units. Find the length of each segment whose endpoints are G and the points of tangency on $\overline{GH}$ and $\overline{GI}$.

10. _____

11. Find x.

11. _____

12. Find x.

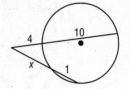

12. _____

For Questions 13–16, use $\odot O$ with $\triangle PQR$ circumscribed.

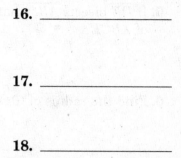

13. Find $m\angle PQR$.

13. _____

14. Find $m\angle XYZ$.

14. _____

15. Find $m\angle PYX$.

15. _____

16. Find $m\angle XUZ$.

16. _____

17. Write the equation of the circle with its center at $(-7, 8)$ and radius of 9.

17. _____

18. Write the equation of the circle containing the point $(8, 1)$ and a center at $(4, -9)$.

18. _____

19. Find the radius of a circle with an equation of $(x + 3)^2 + (y - 2)^2 = r^2$ and containing $(0, 8)$.

19. _____

20. Graph $(x - 3)^2 + (y + 1)^2 = 25$.

20.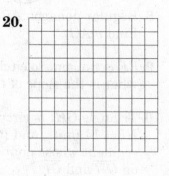

Bonus Find the coordinates of the point(s) of intersection of the circles whose equations are $(x - 2)^2 + y^2 = 13$ and $(x + 3)^2 + y^2 = 8$.

B: _____

10   Chapter 10 Test, Form 3

1. Find *BC*.

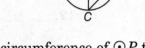

1. _____

2. Find the circumference of ⊙*P* to the nearest hundredth.

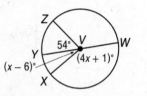

2. _____

3. Find *m*$\widehat{XW}$.

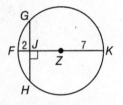

3. _____

4. If the length of an arc of measure 80 is 12π inches, find the length of the radius of the circle.

4. _____

5. Find *GH*.

5. _____

6. Two parallel chords 16 centimeters and 30 centimeters long are 23 centimeters apart. Find the length of the radius of the circle.

6. _____

7. Find *x*.

7. _____

8. The four corners of a square chessboard touch the edge of a round table. The length of the chessboard is 1 foot. Find the length of the radius of the table.

8. _____

9. In ⊙*O*, $\overline{OA}$ and $\overline{OB}$ are radii and *m*∠*BOA* = 120. Tangents $\overline{PA}$ and $\overline{PB}$ have length 10. Find *OA*.

9. _____

10. Quadrilateral *ABCD* is circumscribed about ⊙*O*. If *AB* = 7, *BC* = 11, and *DC* = 8, find *AD*.

10. _____

11. Find *x*.

11. _____

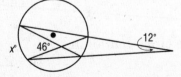

Assessment

For Questions 12–14, use ⊙D with tangents $\overrightarrow{AS}$ and $\overrightarrow{AM}$.

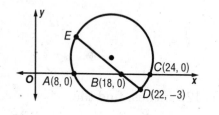

12. Find $m\angle GAF$.

12. _____

13. Find $m\angle GMH$.

13. _____

14. Find $m\angle AEM$.

14. _____

15. Find BE.

15. _____

16. If $\overrightarrow{CD}$ is tangent to ⊙P, find x.

16. _____

17. Find the coordinates of the points of intersection of the line $5x + 6y = 30$ and the circle $x^2 + y^2 = 25$.

17. _____

18. Write the equation of the circle whose center is at $(-3, -2)$ and that is tangent to the y-axis.

18. _____

19. Find the center and radius of the circle whose equation is $x^2 - 12x + y^2 + 14y + 4 = 0$.

19. _____

20. Graph $x^2 + (y + 6)^2 = 1$.

20.

Bonus Find the coordinates of the center of the circle containing the points $(0, 0)$, $(-2, 4)$, and $(4, -2)$.

B: _____

10 Chapter 10 Extended-Response Test

SCORE _____

Demonstrate your knowledge by giving a clear, concise solution to each problem. Be sure to include all relevant drawings and justify your answers. You may show your solution in more than one way or investigate beyond the requirements of the problem.

1. Make up a set of data, perhaps modeling a survey, that you can represent with a circle graph. Calculate the number of degrees for each sector. Draw and label the circle graph. You must have at least four noncongruent sectors on your graph.

2. **a.** Explain the difference between the length of an arc and the measure of an arc.

   b. Is it possible for two arcs to have the same measure but different lengths? Explain your answer.

3. Use a compass to construct a circle. Label the center P. Then draw two chords that are not diameters of $\odot P$. Locate the center of your circle by constructing the perpendicular bisectors of these two chords.

4. An inscribed regular polygon intercepts congruent arcs on the circle. What happens to the measures of these arcs as you increase the number of sides of the polygon?

5. **a.** Write an equation of a circle whose center is not at $(0, 0)$. Write your equation in $(x - h)^2 + (y - k)^2 = r^2$ form.

   b. Find the coordinates of any point B that lies on the circle.

   c. Write an equation of the line through point B that is tangent to the circle. Write your equation in $y = mx + b$ form.

Assessment

10 **Standardized Test Practice**
(Chapters 1–10)

Part 1: Multiple Choice
Instructions: Fill in the appropriate circle for the best answer.

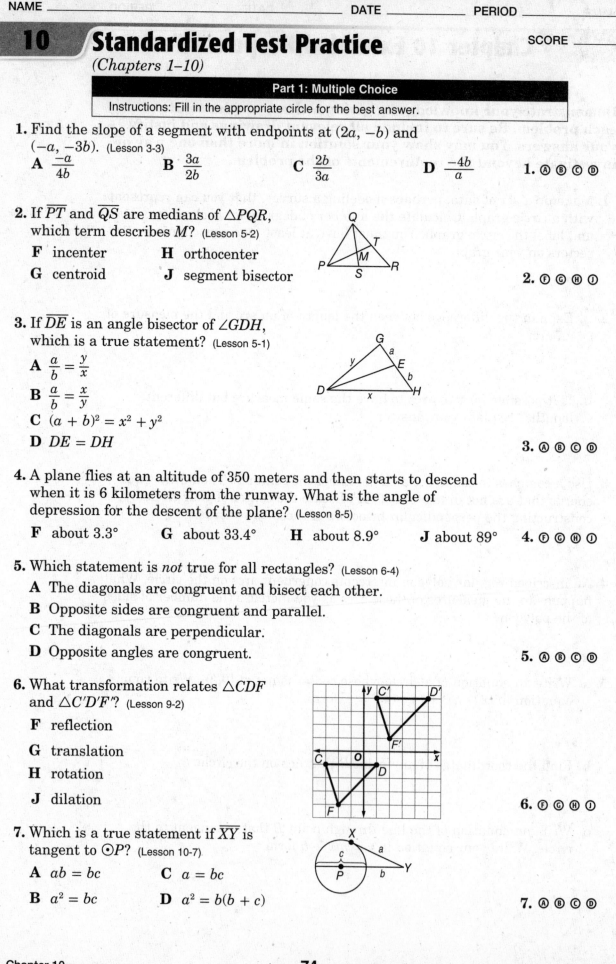

1. Find the slope of a segment with endpoints at $(2a, -b)$ and $(-a, -3b)$. (Lesson 3-3)

   A $\frac{-a}{4b}$ **B** $\frac{3a}{2b}$ **C** $\frac{2b}{3a}$ **D** $\frac{-4b}{a}$ 1. Ⓐ Ⓑ Ⓒ Ⓓ

2. If $\overline{PT}$ and $\overline{QS}$ are medians of $\triangle PQR$, which term describes M? (Lesson 5-2)

   F incenter   **H** orthocenter

   G centroid   **J** segment bisector   2. Ⓕ Ⓖ Ⓗ Ⓙ

3. If $\overline{DE}$ is an angle bisector of $\angle GDH$, which is a true statement? (Lesson 5-1)

   A $\frac{a}{b} = \frac{y}{x}$

   B $\frac{a}{b} = \frac{x}{y}$

   C $(a + b)^2 = x^2 + y^2$

   D $DE = DH$ 3. Ⓐ Ⓑ Ⓒ Ⓓ

4. A plane flies at an altitude of 350 meters and then starts to descend when it is 6 kilometers from the runway. What is the angle of depression for the descent of the plane? (Lesson 8-5)

   F about 3.3°   **G** about 33.4°   **H** about 8.9°   **J** about 89°   4. Ⓕ Ⓖ Ⓗ Ⓙ

5. Which statement is *not* true for all rectangles? (Lesson 6-4)

   A The diagonals are congruent and bisect each other.

   B Opposite sides are congruent and parallel.

   C The diagonals are perpendicular.

   D Opposite angles are congruent.   5. Ⓐ Ⓑ Ⓒ Ⓓ

6. What transformation relates $\triangle CDF$ and $\triangle C'D'F'$? (Lesson 9-2)

   F reflection

   G translation

   H rotation

   J dilation   6. Ⓕ Ⓖ Ⓗ Ⓙ

7. Which is a true statement if $\overline{XY}$ is tangent to $\odot P$? (Lesson 10-7)

   A $ab = bc$ **C** $a = bc$

   B $a^2 = bc$ **D** $a^2 = b(b + c)$ 7. Ⓐ Ⓑ Ⓒ Ⓓ

10 Standardized Test Practice (continued)

Assessment

8. Toby Toy Company sells an average of 560 toys over the Internet each week. There are presently 8500 toys in stock. Which describes how many toys they will have in stock after x weeks if no new toys are added? (Lesson 3-4)

F $y = -560x + 8500$ **H** $y = -8500x + 560$

G $y = 560x + 8500$ **J** $y = 8500x + 560$ 8. Ⓕ Ⓖ Ⓗ Ⓘ

9. Find the value of x. (Lesson 4-2)

A 105   **C** 129.5

B 111   **D** 138   9. Ⓐ Ⓑ Ⓒ Ⓓ

10. Which assumption would you make to start an indirect proof of the statement. *If $3a - 4 < 11$, then $a < 5$.* (Lesson 5-4)

F $a \leq 5$ **G** $a \geq 5$ **H** $a \neq 5$ **J** $a = 5$ 10. Ⓕ Ⓖ Ⓗ Ⓘ

11. Find the images $A(-4, 2)$ and $B(-2, 4)$ under a clockwise rotation of 90° about the origin. (Lesson 9-3)

A $A'(-2, 4)$, $B'(-4, 2)$ **C** $A'(2, 4)$, $B'(4, 2)$

B $A'(4, -2)$, $B'(2, -4)$ **D** $A'(4, 2)$, $B'(2, 4)$ 11. Ⓐ Ⓑ Ⓒ Ⓓ

Part 2: Gridded Response

Instructions: Enter your answer by writing each digit of the answer in a column box and then shading in the appropriate circle that corresponds to that entry.

12. If $ABCD$ is an isosceles trapezoid with bases $\overline{BC}$ and $\overline{AD}$, median $\overline{EF}$, $EF = 43$, and $BC = 12$, find AD. (Lesson 4-6)

13. Find $m\angle 5$. (Lesson 10-6)

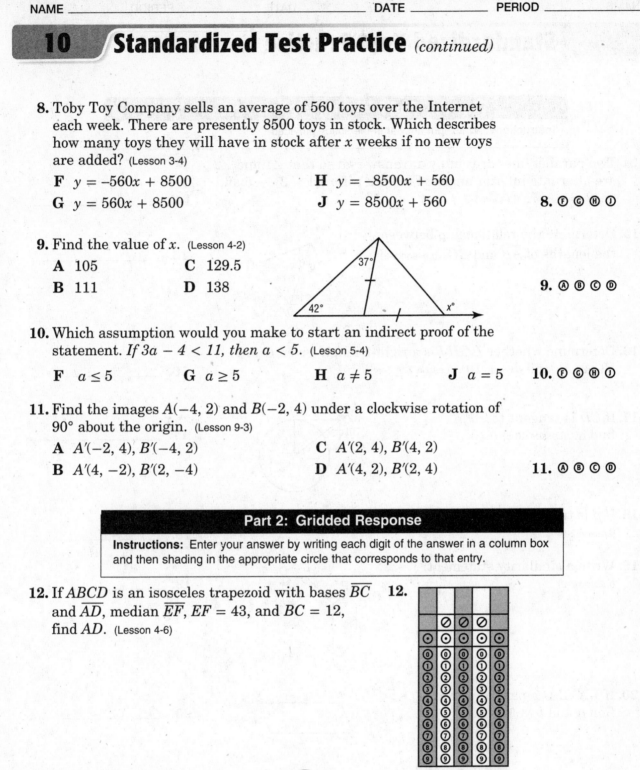

10 **Standardized Test Practice** *(continued)*

Part 3: Short Response

Instructions: Write your answer in the space provided.

14. Two parallel lines are cut by a transversal so that $\angle 1$ and $\angle 2$ are alternate interior angles. Find $m\angle 1$ if $m\angle 1 = 3y - 5$ and $m\angle 2 = y + 7$. (Lesson 3-2)

14. _____

15. Determine the relationship between the lengths of $\overline{AB}$ and $\overline{BC}$. (Lesson 5-3)

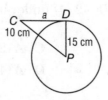

15. _____

16. Determine whether $\triangle GHJ$ is a right triangle given $G(3, 7)$, $H(-2, 5)$, and $J(-4, 10)$. (Lesson 7-2)

16. _____

17. If $\overline{CD}$ is tangent to $\odot P$, find a. (Lesson 10-5)

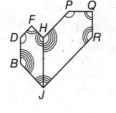

17. _____

18. If p is true and q is false, find the truth value of $p \wedge \sim q$. (Lesson 2-2)

18. _____

19. Write a similarity statement. (Lesson 7-2)

19. _____

20. If $WXYZ$ is a parallelogram, find a and b. (Lesson 6-2)

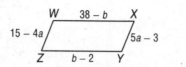

20. _____

21. For the circle with center at $(4, -1)$ and a diameter of 24: (Lesson 10-8)

a. write an equation that represents this circle.

21 **a.** _____

b. find the circumference of the circle.

b. _____

c. find the area of the circle.

c. _____

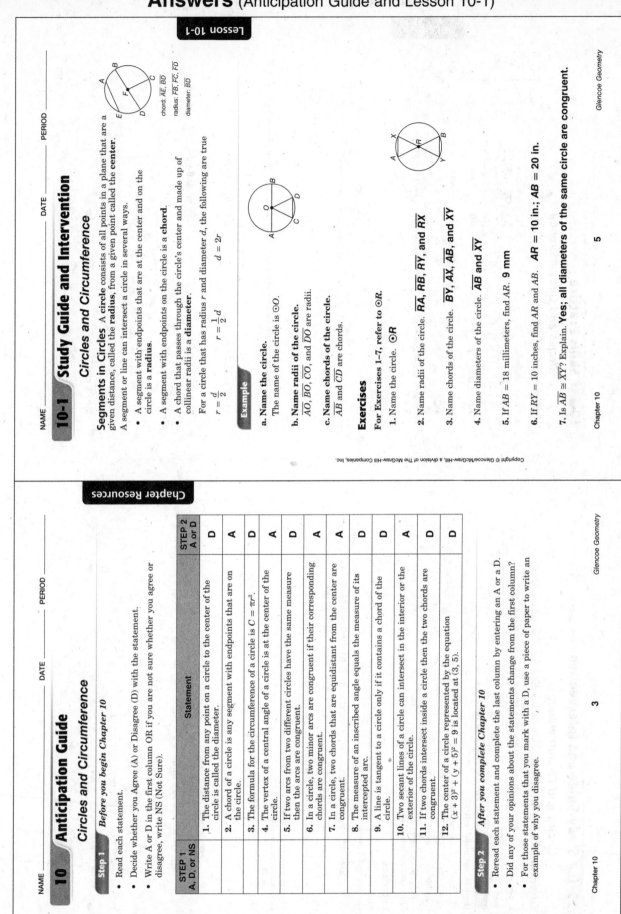

Lesson 10-1

NAME _____ DATE _____ PERIOD _____

10-1 Study Guide and Intervention

Circles and Circumference

Segments in Circles A **circle** consists of all points in a plane that are a given distance, called the **radius**, from a given point called the **center**. A segment or line can intersect a circle in several ways.

- A segment with endpoints that are at the center and on the circle is a **radius**.
- A segment with endpoints on the circle is a **chord**.
- A chord that passes through the circle's center and made up of collinear radii is a **diameter**.

For a circle that has radius r and diameter d, the following are true

$$r = \frac{d}{2} \qquad r = \frac{1}{2}d \qquad d = 2r$$

chord: $\overline{AE}, \overline{BD}$
radius: $\overline{FB}, \overline{FC}, \overline{FD}$
diameter: $\overline{BD}$

Example

a. Name the circle.
The name of the circle is $\odot O$.

b. Name radii of the circle.
$\overline{AO}, \overline{BO}, \overline{CO},$ and $\overline{DO}$ are radii.

c. Name chords of the circle.
$\overline{AB}$ and $\overline{CD}$ are chords.

Exercises

For Exercises 1–7, refer to $\odot R$.

1. Name the circle. **$\odot R$**

2. Name radii of the circle. **$\overline{RA}, \overline{RB}, \overline{RY},$ and $\overline{RX}$**

3. Name chords of the circle. **$\overline{BY}, \overline{AX}, \overline{AB},$ and $\overline{XY}$**

4. Name diameters of the circle. **$\overline{AB}$ and $\overline{XY}$**

5. If $AB = 18$ millimeters, find AR. **9 mm**

6. If $RY = 10$ inches, find AR and AB. **$AR = 10$ in.; $AB = 20$ in.**

7. Is $\overline{AB} \cong \overline{XY}$? Explain. **Yes; all diameters of the same circle are congruent.**

Chapter 10   5   Glencoe Geometry

Chapter Resources

NAME _____ DATE _____ PERIOD _____

10 Anticipation Guide

Circles and Circumference

Step 1 **Before you begin Chapter 10**

- Read each statement.
- Decide whether you Agree (A) or Disagree (D) with the statement.
- Write A or D in the first column OR if you are not sure whether you agree or disagree, write NS (Not Sure).

STEP 1 A, D, or NS	Statement	STEP 2 A or D
	1. The distance from any point on a circle to the center of the circle is called the diameter.	D
	2. A chord of a circle is any segment with endpoints that are on the circle.	A
	3. The formula for the circumference of a circle is $C = \pi r^2$.	D
	4. The vertex of a central angle of a circle is at the center of the circle.	A
	5. If two arcs from two different circles have the same measure then the arcs are congruent.	D
	6. In a circle, two minor arcs are congruent if their corresponding chords are congruent.	A
	7. In a circle, two chords that are equidistant from the center are congruent.	A
	8. The measure of an inscribed angle equals the measure of its intercepted arc.	D
	9. A line is tangent to a circle only if it contains a chord of the circle.	D
	10. Two secant lines of a circle can intersect in the interior or the exterior of the circle.	A
	11. If two chords intersect inside a circle then the two chords are congruent.	D
	12. The center of a circle represented by the equation $(x + 3)^2 + (y + 5)^2 = 9$ is located at $(3, 5)$.	D

Step 2 **After you complete Chapter 10**

- Reread each statement and complete the last column by entering an A or a D.
- Did any of your opinions about the statements change from the first column?
- For those statements that you mark with a D, use a piece of paper to write an example of why you disagree.

Chapter 10   3   Glencoe Geometry

Answers

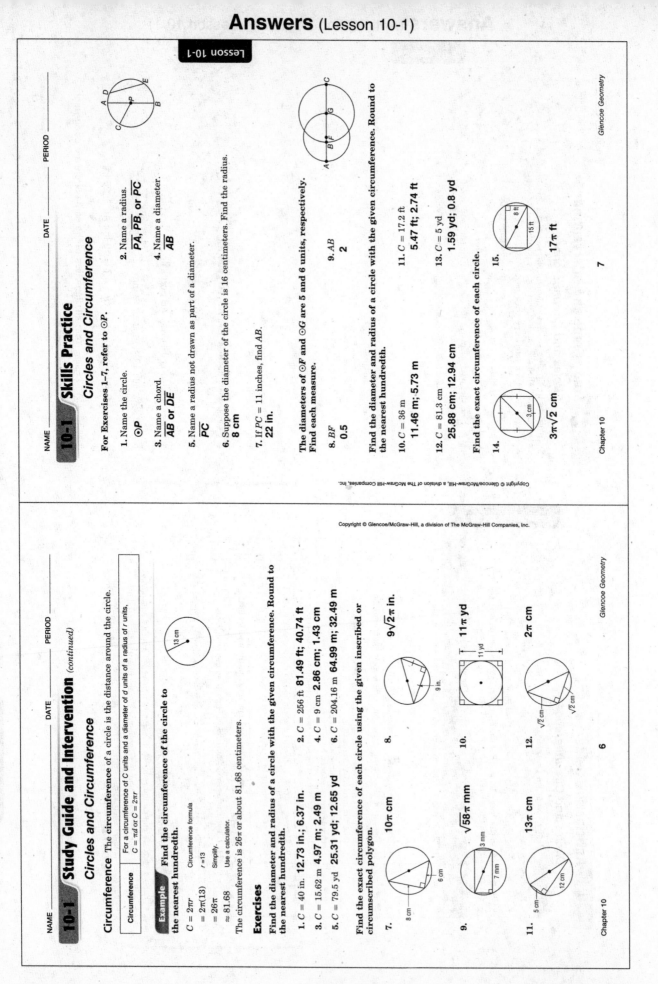

NAME _____ DATE _____ PERIOD _____

10-1 Skills Practice

Circles and Circumference

For Exercises 1–7, refer to ⊙P.

1. Name the circle.
⊙P

2. Name a radius.
$\overline{PA}$, $\overline{PB}$, or $\overline{PC}$

3. Name a chord.
$\overline{AB}$ or $\overline{DE}$

4. Name a diameter.
$\overline{AB}$

5. Name a radius not drawn as part of a diameter.
$\overline{PC}$

6. Suppose the diameter of the circle is 16 centimeters. Find the radius.
8 cm

7. If PC = 11 inches, find AB.
22 in.

The diameters of ⊙F and ⊙G are 5 and 6 units, respectively. Find each measure.

8. BF
0.5

9. AB
2

Find the diameter and radius of a circle with the given circumference. Round to the nearest hundredth.

10. C = 36 m
11.46 m; 5.73 m

11. C = 17.2 ft
5.47 ft; 2.74 ft

12. C = 81.3 cm
25.88 cm; 12.94 cm

13. C = 5 yd
1.59 yd; 0.8 yd

Find the exact circumference of each circle.

14. $3\pi\sqrt{2}$ cm

15. 17π ft

Chapter 10   7   *Glencoe Geometry*

NAME _____ DATE _____ PERIOD _____

10-1 Study Guide and Intervention (continued)

Circles and Circumference

Circumference The circumference of a circle is the distance around the circle.

| Circumference | For a circumference of C units and a diameter of d units or a radius of r units, $C = \pi d$ or $C = 2\pi r$ |

Example Find the circumference of the circle to the nearest hundredth.

$C = 2\pi r$ Circumference formula
$= 2\pi(13)$ $r = 13$
$= 26\pi$ Simplify.
≈ 81.68 Use a calculator.

The circumference is 26π or about 81.68 centimeters.

Exercises

Find the diameter and radius of a circle with the given circumference. Round to the nearest hundredth.

1. C = 40 in. 12.73 in.; 6.37 in.
2. C = 256 ft 81.49 ft; 40.74 ft
3. C = 15.62 m 4.97 m; 2.49 m
4. C = 9 cm 2.86 cm; 1.43 cm
5. C = 79.5 yd 25.31 yd; 12.65 yd
6. C = 204.16 m 64.99 m; 32.49 m

Find the exact circumference of each circle using the given inscribed or circumscribed polygon.

7. 10π cm

8. $9\sqrt{2}\pi$ in.

9. $\sqrt{58}\pi$ mm

10. 11π yd

11. 13π cm

12. 2π cm

Chapter 10   6   *Glencoe Geometry*

Chapter 10   **A2**   *Glencoe Geometry*

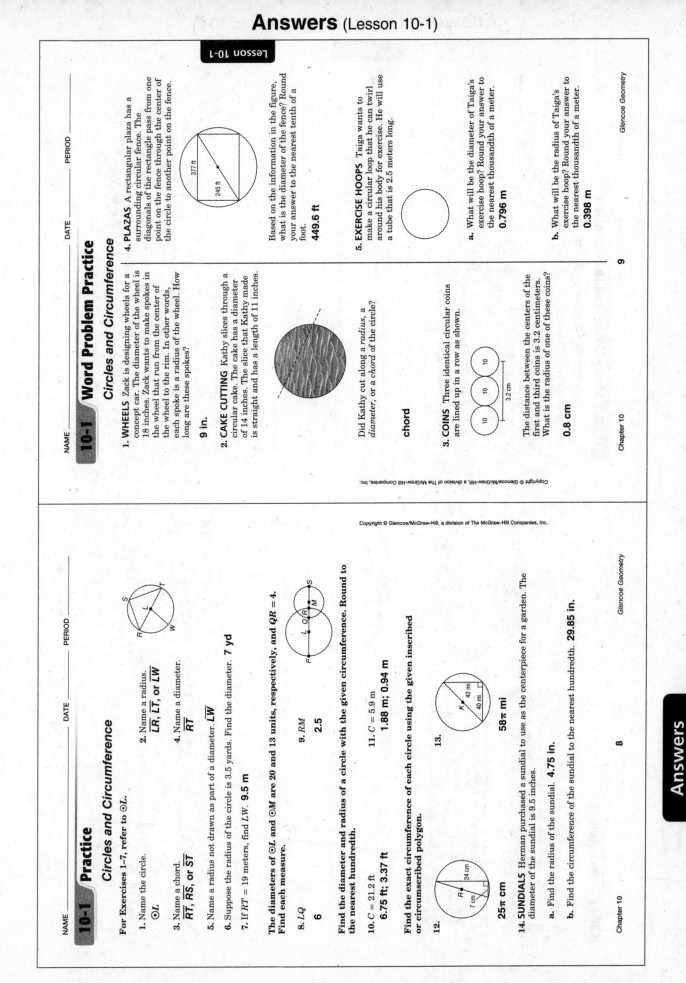

NAME _____ DATE _____ PERIOD _____

10-1 Practice

Circles and Circumference

For Exercises 1–7, refer to ⊙L.

1. Name the circle.
   ⊙L

2. Name a radius.
   $\overline{LR}$, $\overline{LT}$, or $\overline{LW}$

3. Name a chord.
   $\overline{RT}$, $\overline{RS}$, or $\overline{ST}$

4. Name a diameter.
   $\overline{RT}$

5. Name a radius not drawn as part of a diameter. **$\overline{LW}$**

6. Suppose the radius of the circle is 3.5 yards. Find the diameter. **7 yd**

7. If $RT = 19$ meters, find LW. **9.5 m**

The diameters of ⊙L and ⊙M are 20 and 13 units, respectively, and $QR = 4$. Find each measure.

8. LQ
   6

9. RM
   2.5

Find the diameter and radius of a circle with the given circumference. Round to the nearest hundredth.

10. $C = 21.2$ ft
    6.75 ft; 3.37 ft

11. $C = 5.9$ m
    1.88 m; 0.94 m

Find the exact circumference of each circle using the given inscribed or circumscribed polygon.

12.
    25π cm

13.
    58π mi

14. **SUNDIALS** Herman purchased a sundial to use as the centerpiece for a garden. The diameter of the sundial is 9.5 inches.

   a. Find the radius of the sundial. **4.75 in.**

   b. Find the circumference of the sundial to the nearest hundredth. **29.85 in.**

NAME _____ DATE _____ PERIOD _____

10-1 Word Problem Practice

Circles and Circumference

1. **WHEELS** Zack is designing wheels for a concept car. The diameter of the wheel is 18 inches. Zack wants to make spokes in the wheel that run from the center of the wheel to the rim. In other words, each spoke is a radius of the wheel. How long are these spokes?
   9 in.

2. **CAKE CUTTING** Kathy slices through a circular cake. The cake has a diameter of 14 inches. The slice that Kathy made is straight and has a length of 11 inches.

   Did Kathy cut along a *radius*, a *diameter*, or a *chord* of the circle?

   chord

3. **COINS** Three identical circular coins are lined up in a row as shown.

   The distance between the centers of the first and third coins is 3.2 centimeters. What is the radius of one of these coins?
   0.8 cm

4. **PLAZAS** A rectangular plaza has a surrounding circular fence. The diagonals of the rectangle pass from one point on the fence through the center of the circle to another point on the fence.

   Based on the information in the figure, what is the diameter of the fence? Round your answer to the nearest tenth of a foot.
   449.6 ft

5. **EXERCISE HOOPS** Taiga wants to make a circular loop that he can twirl around his body for exercise. He will use a tube that is 2.5 meters long.

   a. What will be the diameter of Taiga's exercise hoop? Round your answer to the nearest thousandth of a meter.
   0.796 m

   b. What will be the radius of Taiga's exercise hoop? Round your answer to the nearest thousandth of a meter.
   0.398 m

Answers

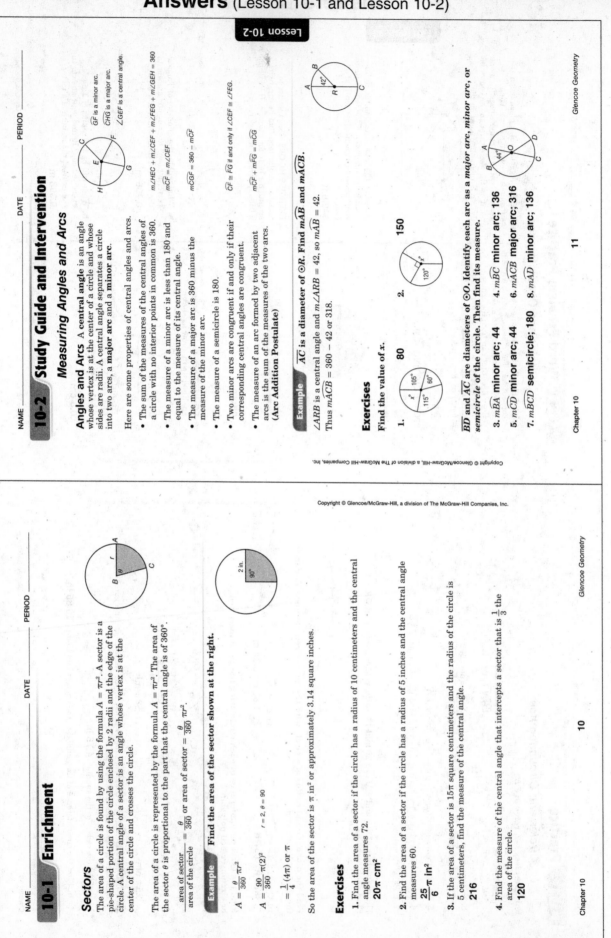

Lesson 10-2

NAME _____ DATE _____ PERIOD _____

10-2 Study Guide and Intervention
Measuring Angles and Arcs

Angles and Arcs A **central angle** is an angle whose vertex is at the center of a circle and whose sides are radii. A central angle separates a circle into two arcs, a **major arc** and a **minor arc**.

$\overarc{GF}$ is a minor arc.
$\overarc{CHG}$ is a major arc.
$\angle GEF$ is a central angle.

Here are some properties of central angles and arcs.

- The sum of the measures of the central angles of a circle with no interior points in common is 360. $m\angle HEC + m\angle CEF + m\angle FEG + m\angle GEH = 360$
- The measure of a minor arc is less than 180 and equal to the measure of its central angle. $m\overarc{CF} = m\angle CEF$
- The measure of a major arc is 360 minus the measure of the minor arc. $m\overarc{CGF} = 360 - m\overarc{CF}$
- The measure of a semicircle is 180.
- Two minor arcs are congruent if and only if their corresponding central angles are congruent. $\overarc{CF} \cong \overarc{FG}$ if and only if $\angle CEF \cong \angle FEG$.
- The measure of an arc formed by two adjacent arcs is the sum of the measures of the two arcs. (Arc Addition Postulate) $m\overarc{CF} + m\overarc{FG} = m\overarc{CG}$

Example $\overline{AC}$ is a diameter of $\odot R$. Find $m\overarc{AB}$ and $m\overarc{ACB}$.

$\angle ARB$ is a central angle and $m\angle ARB = 42$, so $m\overarc{AB} = 42$.
Thus $m\overarc{ACB} = 360 - 42$ or 318.

Exercises
Find the value of x.
1. 80
2. 150

$\overline{BD}$ and $\overline{AC}$ are diameters of $\odot O$. Identify each arc as a *major arc, minor arc,* or *semicircle* of the circle. Then find its measure.

3. $m\overarc{BA}$ minor arc; 44
4. $m\overarc{BC}$ minor arc; 136
5. $m\overarc{CD}$ minor arc; 44
6. $m\overarc{ACB}$ major arc; 316
7. $m\overarc{BCD}$ semicircle; 180
8. $m\overarc{AD}$ minor arc; 136

Chapter 10   11   *Glencoe Geometry*

NAME _____ DATE _____ PERIOD _____

10-1 Enrichment
Sectors

The area of a circle is found by using the formula $A = \pi r^2$. A **sector** is a pie-shaped portion of the circle enclosed by 2 radii and the edge of the circle. A central angle of a sector is an angle whose vertex is at the center of the circle and crosses the circle.

The area of a circle is represented by the formula $A = \pi r^2$. The area of the sector θ is proportional to the part that the central angle is of 360°.

$$\frac{\text{area of sector}}{\text{area of the circle}} = \frac{\theta}{360}\,\pi r^2 \quad \text{or} \quad \text{area of sector} = \frac{\theta}{360}\,\pi r^2.$$

Example Find the area of the sector shown at the right.

$A = \frac{\theta}{360}\,\pi r^2$

$A = \frac{90}{360}\,\pi(2)^2$ $r = 2, \theta = 90$

$= \frac{1}{4}(4\pi)$ or π

So the area of the sector is π in² or approximately 3.14 square inches.

Exercises
1. Find the area of a sector if the circle has a radius of 10 centimeters and the central angle measures 72.
20π cm²

2. Find the area of a sector if the circle has a radius of 5 inches and the central angle measures 60.
$\frac{25}{6}$ in²

3. If the area of a sector is 15π square centimeters and the radius of the circle is 5 centimeters, find the measure of the central angle.
216

4. Find the measure of the central angle that intercepts a sector that is $\frac{1}{3}$ the area of the circle.
120

Chapter 10   10   *Glencoe Geometry*

NAME _____ DATE _____ PERIOD _____

10-2 Study Guide and Intervention (continued)

Measuring Angles and Arcs

Arc Length An arc is part of a circle and its length is a part of the circumference of the circle.

The length of arc ℓ can be found using the following equation:

$$\ell = \frac{x}{360} \cdot 2\pi r$$

Example Find the length of $\widehat{AB}$. Round to the nearest hundredth.

The length of arc $\widehat{AB}$, can be found using the following equation: $\widehat{AB} = \frac{x}{360} \cdot 2\pi r$

$\widehat{AB} = \frac{x}{360} \cdot 2\pi r$ Arc Length Equation

$\widehat{AB} = \frac{135}{360} \cdot 2\pi(8)$ Substitution

$\widehat{AB} \approx 18.85$ in.   Use a calculator.

Exercises

Use ⊙O to find the length of each arc. Round to the nearest hundredth.

1. $\widehat{DE}$ if the radius is 2 meters **4.19 m**

2. $\widehat{DEA}$ if the diameter is 7 inches **12.83 in.**

3. $\widehat{BC}$ if BE = 24 feet **9.42 ft**

4. $\widehat{CBA}$ if DO = 3 millimeters **7.07 mm**

Use ⊙P to find the length of each arc. Round to the nearest hundredth.

5. $\widehat{RT}$, if MT = 7 yards **3.05 yd**

6. $\widehat{MR}$, if PR = 13 feet **29.50 ft**

7. $\widehat{MST}$, if MP = 2 inches **6.28 in.**

8. $\widehat{MRS}$, if PS = 10 centimeters **40.14 cm**

Chapter 10   12   Glencoe Geometry

NAME _____ DATE _____ PERIOD _____

10-2 Skills Practice

Measuring Angles and Arcs

$\overline{AC}$ and $\overline{EB}$ are diameters of ⊙R. Identify each arc as a *major arc*, *minor arc*, or *semicircle* of the circle. Then find its measure.

1. $m\widehat{EA}$ **minor arc; 50**

2. $m\widehat{CB}$ **minor arc; 50**

3. $m\widehat{DC}$ **minor arc; 100**

4. $m\widehat{DEB}$ **major arc; 210**

5. $m\widehat{AB}$ **minor arc; 130**

6. $m\widehat{CDA}$ **semicircle; 180**

$\overline{PR}$ and $\overline{QT}$ are diameters of ⊙A. Find each measure.

7. $m\widehat{UPQ}$ **130**

8. $m\widehat{PQR}$ **180**

9. $m\widehat{UTS}$ **90**

10. $m\widehat{RS}$ **50**

11. $m\widehat{RSU}$ **140**

12. $m\widehat{STP}$ **130**

13. $m\widehat{PQS}$ **230**

14. $m\widehat{PRU}$ **320**

Use ⊙D to find the length of each arc. Round to the nearest hundredth.

15. $\widehat{LM}$ if the radius is 5 inches **8.73 in.**

16. $\widehat{MN}$ if the diameter is 3 yards **2.09 yd**

17. $\widehat{KL}$ if JD = 7 centimeters **7.33 cm**

18. $\widehat{NJK}$ if NL = 12 feet **12.57 ft**

19. $\widehat{KLM}$ if DM = 9 millimeters **25.13 mm**

20. $\widehat{JK}$ if KD = 15 inches **13.09 in.**

Chapter 10   13   Glencoe Geometry

Answers (Lesson 10-2)

NAME _____ DATE _____ PERIOD _____

10-2 Word Problem Practice

Measuring Angles and Arcs

1. CONDIMENTS A number of people in a park were asked to name their favorite condiment for hot dogs. The results are shown in the circle graph.

Ketchup 198°
Mustard 111.9°
Relish 29.4°
Mayonnaise 16.1°
Other 4.6°

What was the second most popular hot dog condiment?

mustard

2. CLOCKS Shiatsu is a Japanese massage technique. One of the beliefs is that various body functions are most active at various times during the day. To illustrate this, they use a Chinese clock that is based on a circle divided into 12 equal sections by radii.

What is the measure of any one of the 12 equal central angles?

30

3. PIES Yolanda has divided a circular apple pie into 4 slices by cutting the pie along 4 radii. The central angles of the 4 slices are $3x$, $6x - 10$, $4x + 10$, and $5x$ degrees. What exactly are the numerical measures of the central angles?

60, 110, 90, and 100

4. RIBBONS Cora is wrapping a ribbon around a cylinder-shaped gift box. The box has a diameter of 15 inches and the ribbon is 60 inches long. Cora is able to wrap the ribbon all the way around the box once, and then continue so that the second end of the ribbon passes the first end. What is the central angle formed between the ends of the ribbon? Round your answer to the nearest tenth of a degree.

98.4°

5. BIKE WHEELS Lucy has to buy a new wheel for her bike. The bike wheel has a diameter of 20 inches.

a. If Lucy rolls the wheel one complete rotation along the ground, how far will the wheel travel? Round your answer to the nearest hundredth of an inch.

62.83 in.

b. If the bike wheel is rolled along the ground so that it rotates 45°, how far will the wheel travel? Round your answer to the nearest hundredth of an inch.

7.85 in.

c. If the bike wheel is rolled along the ground for 10 inches, through what angle does the wheel rotate? Round your answer to the nearest tenth of a degree.

57.3

Chapter 10   15   Glencoe Geometry

NAME _____ DATE _____ PERIOD _____

10-2 Practice

Measuring Angles and Arcs

$\overline{AC}$ and $\overline{DB}$ are diameters of $\odot Q$. Identify each arc as a *major arc*, *minor arc*, or *semicircle* of the circle. Then find its measure.

1. $m\widehat{AE}$ **minor arc; 50**

2. $m\widehat{AB}$ **minor arc; 80**

3. $m\widehat{EDC}$ **minor arc; 130**

4. $m\widehat{ADC}$ **semicircle; 180**

5. $m\widehat{ABC}$ **semicircle; 180**

6. $m\widehat{BC}$ **minor arc; 100**

$\overline{FH}$ and $\overline{EG}$ are diameters of $\odot P$. Find each measure.

7. $m\widehat{EF}$ **38**

8. $m\widehat{DE}$ **52**

9. $m\widehat{FG}$ **142**

10. $m\widehat{DHG}$ **128**

11. $m\widehat{DFG}$ **232**

12. $m\widehat{DGE}$ **308**

Use $\odot Z$ to find each arc length. Round to the nearest hundredth.

13. $\widehat{QPT}$, if $QZ = 10$ inches
20.94 in.

14. $\widehat{QR}$, if $PZ = 12$ feet
12.57 ft

15. $\widehat{PQR}$, if $TR = 15$ meters
19.63 m

16. $\widehat{QPS}$, if $ZQ = 7$ centimeters
17.10 cm

17. HOMEWORK Refer to the table, which shows the number of hours students at Leland High School say they spend on homework each night.

Homework	
Less than 1 hour	8%
1–2 hours	29%
2–3 hours	58%
3–4 hours	3%
Over 4 hours	2%

a. If you were to construct a circle graph of the data, how many degrees would be allotted to each category?
28.8, 104.4, 208.8, 10.8, 7.2

b. Describe the arcs associated with each category.

The arc associated with 2–3 hours is a major arc; minor arcs are associated with the remaining categories.

Chapter 10   14   Glencoe Geometry

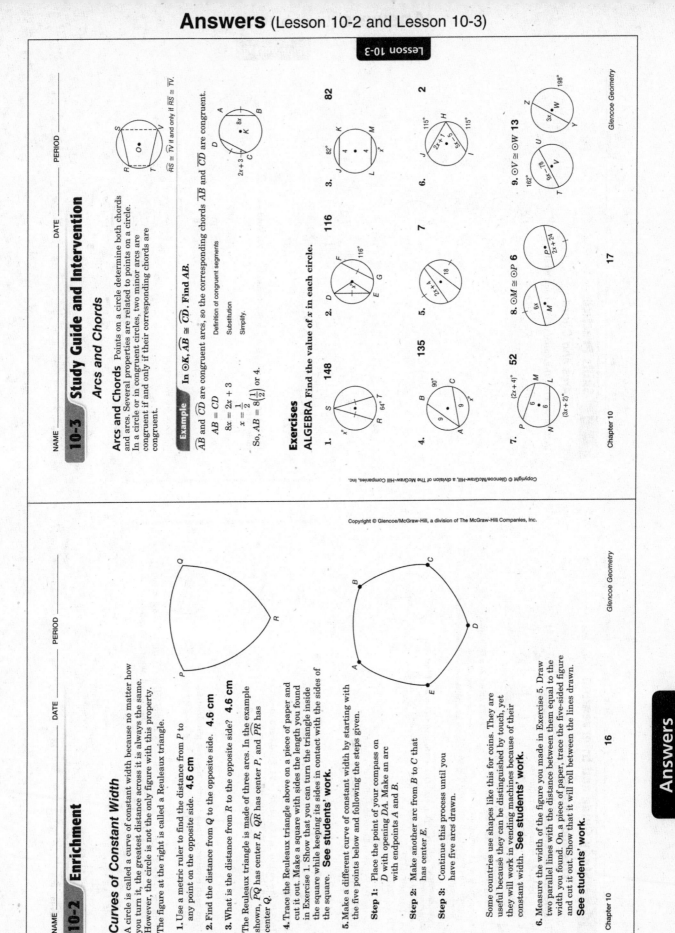

NAME _____ DATE _____ PERIOD _____

10-3 Study Guide and Intervention

Arcs and Chords

Arcs and Chords Points on a circle determine both chords and arcs. Several properties are related to points on a circle. In a circle or in congruent circles, two minor arcs are congruent if and only if their corresponding chords are congruent.

Example In $\odot K$, $\widehat{AB} \cong \widehat{CD}$. Find AB.

$\widehat{AB}$ and $\widehat{CD}$ are congruent arcs, so the corresponding chords $\overline{AB}$ and $\overline{CD}$ are congruent.

$AB = CD$	Definition of congruent segments
$8x = 2x + 3$	Substitution
$x = \frac{1}{2}$	Simplify.

So, $AB = 8\left(\frac{1}{2}\right)$ or 4.

Exercises

ALGEBRA Find the value of x in each circle.

1. **148**

2. **116**

3. **82**

4. **135**

5. **7**

6. **2**

7. $\odot P \cong \odot M$ **52**

8. $\odot M \cong \odot P$ **6**

9. $\odot V \cong \odot W$ **13**

$\widehat{RS} \cong \widehat{TV}$ if and only if $\overline{RS} \cong \overline{TV}$.

NAME _____ DATE _____ PERIOD _____

10-2 Enrichment

Curves of Constant Width

A circle is called a curve of constant width because no matter how you turn it, the greatest distance across it is always the same. However, the circle is not the only figure with this property. The figure at the right is called a Reuleaux triangle.

1. Use a metric ruler to find the distance from P to any point on the opposite side. **4.6 cm**

2. Find the distance from Q to the opposite side. **4.6 cm**

3. What is the distance from R to the opposite side? **4.6 cm**

The Reuleaux triangle is made of three arcs. In the example shown, PQ has center R, QR has center P, and PR has center Q.

4. Trace the Reuleaux triangle above on a piece of paper and cut it out. Make a square with sides the length you found in Exercise 1. Show that you can turn the triangle inside the square while keeping its sides in contact with the sides of the square. **See students' work.**

5. Make a different curve of constant width by starting with the five points below and following the steps given.

Step 1: Place the point of your compass on D with opening DA. Make an arc with endpoints A and B.

Step 2: Make another arc from B to C that has center E.

Step 3: Continue this process until you have five arcs drawn.

Some countries use shapes like this for coins. They are useful because they can be distinguished by touch, yet they will work in vending machines because of their constant width. **See students' work.**

6. Measure the width of the figure you made in Exercise 5. Draw two parallel lines with the distance between them equal to the width you found. On a piece of paper, trace the five-sided figure and cut it out. Show that it will roll between the lines drawn. **See students' work.**

Answers

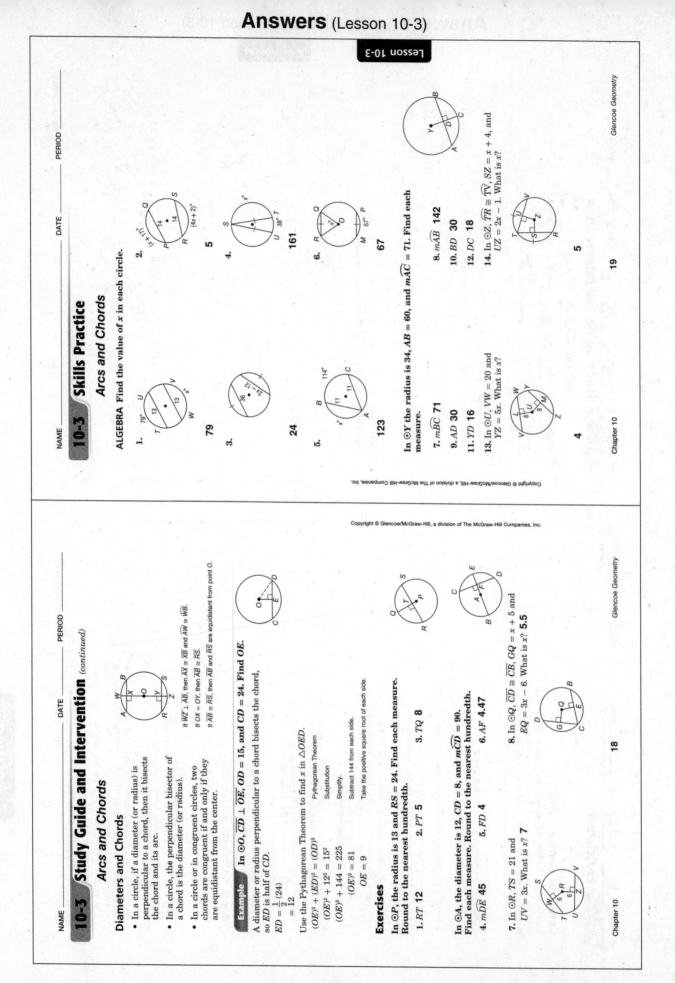

10-3 Study Guide and Intervention (continued)

Arcs and Chords

Diameters and Chords

- In a circle, if a diameter (or radius) is perpendicular to a chord, then it bisects the chord and its arc.

- In a circle, the perpendicular bisector of a chord is the diameter (or radius).

- In a circle or in congruent circles, two chords are congruent if and only if they are equidistant from the center.

If $\overline{WZ} \perp \overline{AB}$, then $\overline{AX} \cong \overline{XB}$ and $\overline{AW} \cong \overline{WB}$.

If $OX = OY$, then $\overline{AB} \cong \overline{RS}$.

If $\overline{AB} \cong \overline{RS}$, then $\overline{AB}$ and $\overline{RS}$ are equidistant from point O.

Example In $\odot O$, $\overline{CD} \perp \overline{OE}$, $OD = 15$, and $CD = 24$. Find OE.

A diameter or radius perpendicular to a chord bisects the chord, so ED is half of CD.

$ED = \frac{1}{2}(24)$
$= 12$

Use the Pythagorean Theorem to find x in $\triangle OED$.

$(OE)^2 + (ED)^2 = (OD)^2$ Pythagorean Theorem
$(OE)^2 + 12^2 = 15^2$ Substitution
$(OE)^2 + 144 = 225$ Simplify.
$(OE)^2 = 81$ Subtract 144 from each side.
$OE = 9$ Take the positive square root of each side.

Exercises

In $\odot P$, the radius is 13 and $RS = 24$. Find each measure. Round to the nearest hundredth.

1. RT **12**   2. PT **5**   3. TQ **8**

In $\odot A$, the diameter is 12, $CD = 8$, and $m\overset{\frown}{CD} = 90$. Find each measure. Round to the nearest hundredth.

4. $m\overset{\frown}{DE}$ **45**   5. FD **4**   6. AF **4.47**

7. In $\odot R$, $TS = 21$ and $UV = 3x$. What is x? **7**

8. In $\odot Q$, $\overline{CD} \cong \overline{CB}$, $GQ = x + 5$ and $EQ = 3x - 6$. What is x? **5.5**

NAME _____ DATE _____ PERIOD _____

10-3 Skills Practice

Arcs and Chords

ALGEBRA Find the value of x in each circle.

1. **79**

2. **5**

3. **24**

4. **161**

5. **123**

6. **67**

In $\odot Y$ the radius is 34, $AB = 60$, and $m\overset{\frown}{AC} = 71$. Find each measure.

7. $m\overset{\frown}{BC}$ **71**

8. $m\overset{\frown}{AB}$ **142**

9. AD **30**

10. BD **30**

11. YD **16**

12. DC **18**

13. In $\odot U$, $VW = 20$ and $YZ = 5x$. What is x? **4**

14. In $\odot Z$, $\overline{TR} \cong \overline{TV}$, $SZ = x + 4$, and $UZ = 2x - 1$. What is x? **5**

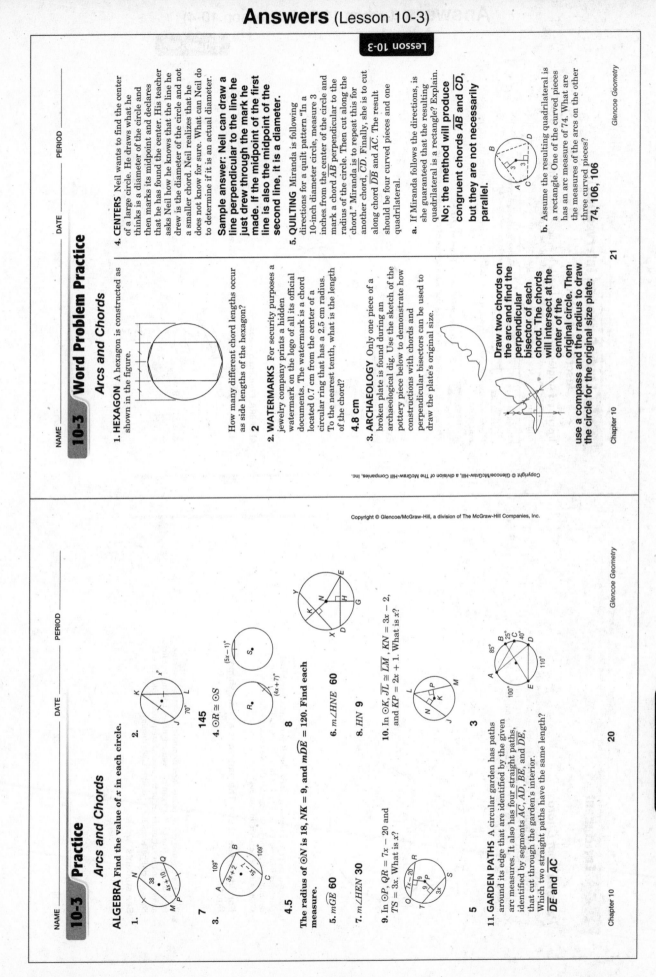

NAME _____ DATE _____ PERIOD _____

10-3 Practice

Arcs and Chords

ALGEBRA Find the value of x in each circle.

1.

2.

7

4.5

3.

4. ⊙R ≅ ⊙S

145

8

The radius of ⊙N is 18, NK = 9, and m$\widehat{DE}$ = 120. Find each measure.

5. m$\widehat{GE}$ **60**

6. m∠HNE **60**

7. m∠HEN **30**

8. HN **9**

9. In ⊙P, QR = 7x − 20 and TS = 3x. What is x?

5

10. In ⊙K, $\overline{JL} ≅ \overline{LM}$, KN = 3x − 2, and KP = 2x + 1. What is x?

3

11. **GARDEN PATHS** A circular garden has paths around its edge that are identified by the given arc measures. It also has four straight paths, identified by segments $\overline{AC}$, $\overline{AD}$, $\overline{BE}$, and $\overline{DE}$, that cut through the garden's interior. Which two straight paths have the same length? $\overline{DE}$ and $\overline{AC}$

Chapter 10

20

Glencoe Geometry

NAME _____ DATE _____ PERIOD _____

10-3 Word Problem Practice

Arcs and Chords

1. **HEXAGON** A hexagon is constructed as shown in the figure.

How many different chord lengths occur as side lengths of the hexagon? **2**

2. **WATERMARKS** For security purposes a jewelry company prints a hidden watermark on the logo of all its official documents. The watermark is a chord located 0.7 cm from the center of a circular ring that has a 2.5 cm radius. To the nearest tenth, what is the length of the chord? **4.8 cm**

3. **ARCHAEOLOGY** Only one piece of a broken plate is found during an archaeological dig. Use the sketch of the pottery piece below to demonstrate how constructions with chords and perpendicular bisectors can be used to draw the plate's original size.

Draw two chords on the arc and find the perpendicular bisector of each chord. The chords will intersect at the center of the original circle. Then use a compass and the radius to draw the circle for the original size plate.

4. **CENTERS** Neil wants to find the center of a large circle. He draws what he thinks is a diameter of the circle and then marks its midpoint and declares that he has found the center. His teacher asks Neil how he knows that the line he drew is the diameter of the circle and not a smaller chord. Neil realizes that he does not know for sure. What can Neil do to determine if it is an actual diameter.

Sample answer: Neil can draw a line perpendicular to the line he just drew through the mark he made. If the midpoint of the first line is also the midpoint of the second line, it is a diameter.

5. **QUILTING** Miranda is following directions for a quilt pattern "In a 10-inch diameter circle, measure 3 inches from the center of the circle and mark a chord $\overline{AB}$ perpendicular to the radius of the circle. Then cut along the chord." Miranda is to repeat this for another chord, $\overline{CD}$. Finally, she is to cut along chord $\overline{DB}$ and $\overline{AC}$. The result should be four curved pieces and one quadrilateral.

a. If Miranda follows the directions, is she guaranteed that the resulting quadrilateral is a rectangle? Explain. **No; the method will produce congruent chords $\overline{AB}$ and $\overline{CD}$, but they are not necessarily parallel.**

b. Assume the resulting quadrilateral is a rectangle. One of the curved pieces has an arc measure of 74. What are the measures of the arcs on the other three curved pieces? **74, 106, 106**

Chapter 10

21

Glencoe Geometry

Answers

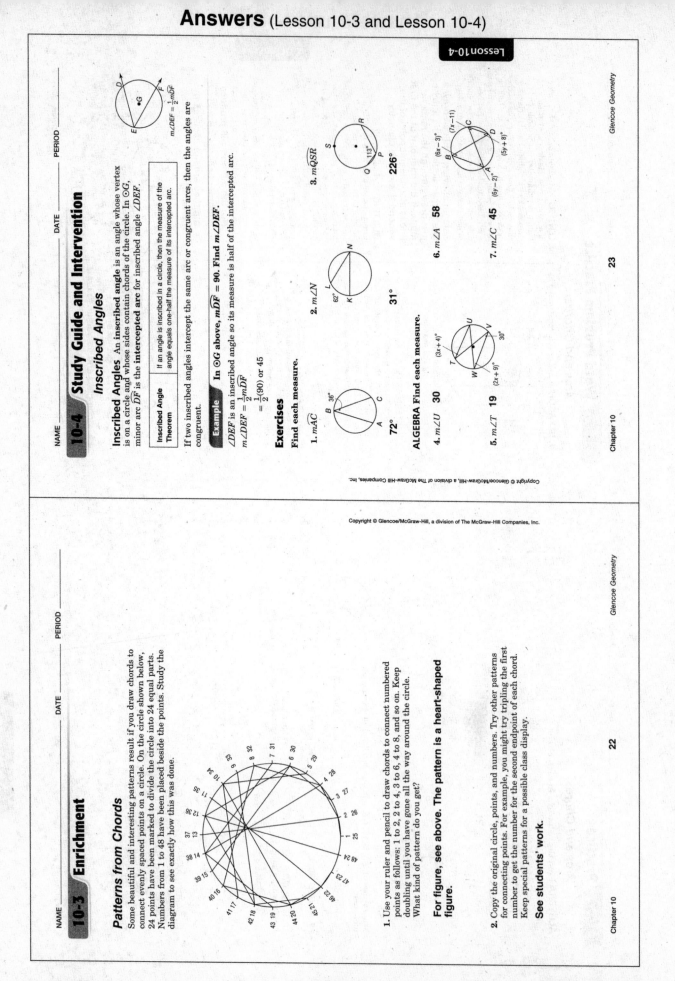

Lesson 10-4

10-4 Study Guide and Intervention

Inscribed Angles

Inscribed Angles An **inscribed angle** is an angle whose vertex is on a circle and whose sides contain chords of the circle. In $\odot G$, minor arc $\overparen{DF}$ is the **intercepted arc** for inscribed angle $\angle DEF$.

Inscribed Angle Theorem	If an angle is inscribed in a circle, then the measure of the angle equals one-half the measure of its intercepted arc.

If two inscribed angles intercept the same arc or congruent arcs, then the angles are congruent.

Example In $\odot G$ above, $m\overparen{DF} = 90$. Find $m\angle DEF$.

$\angle DEF$ is an inscribed angle so its measure is half of the intercepted arc.

$m\angle DEF = \frac{1}{2}m\overparen{DF}$
$= \frac{1}{2}(90)$ or 45

Exercises

Find each measure.

1. $m\overparen{AC}$ **72°**

2. $m\angle N$ **31°**

3. $m\overparen{QSR}$ **226°**

ALGEBRA Find each measure.

4. $m\angle U$ **30**

5. $m\angle T$ **19**

6. $m\angle A$ **58**

7. $m\angle C$ **45**

Chapter 10   23   Glencoe Geometry

10-3 Enrichment

Patterns from Chords

Some beautiful and interesting patterns result if you draw chords to connect evenly spaced points on a circle. On the circle shown below, 24 points have been marked to divide the circle into 24 equal parts. Numbers from 1 to 48 have been placed beside the points. Study the diagram to see exactly how this was done.

1. Use your ruler and pencil to draw chords to connect numbered points as follows: 1 to 2, 2 to 4, 3 to 6, 4 to 8, and so on. Keep doubling until you have gone all the way around the circle. What kind of pattern do you get?

For figure, see above. The pattern is a heart-shaped figure.

2. Copy the original circle, points, and numbers. Try other patterns for connecting points. For example, you might try tripling the first number to get the number for the second endpoint of each chord. Keep special patterns for a possible class display.

See students' work.

Chapter 10   22   Glencoe Geometry

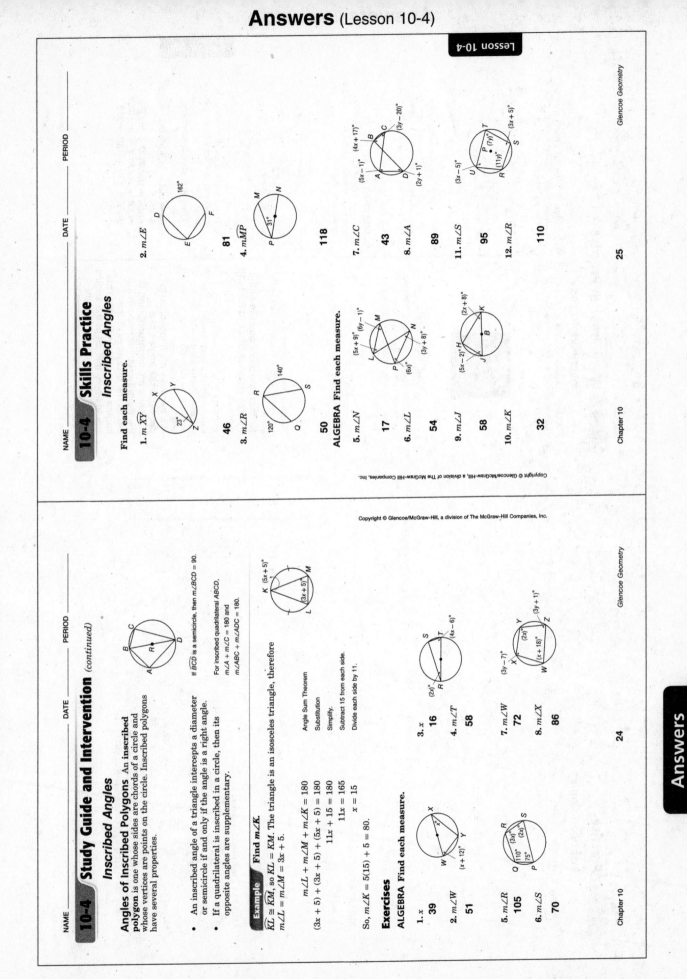

NAME _____ DATE _____ PERIOD _____

10-4 Study Guide and Intervention (continued)

Inscribed Angles

Angles of Inscribed Polygons An inscribed polygon is one whose sides are chords of a circle and whose vertices are points on the circle. Inscribed polygons have several properties.

- An inscribed angle of a triangle intercepts a diameter or semicircle if and only if the angle is a right angle.

  If $\widehat{BCD}$ is a semicircle, then $m\angle BCD = 90$.

- If a quadrilateral is inscribed in a circle, then its opposite angles are supplementary.

  For inscribed quadrilateral $ABCD$,
  $m\angle A + m\angle C = 180$ and
  $m\angle ABC + m\angle ADC = 180$.

Example Find $m\angle K$

$\overline{KL} \cong \overline{KM}$, so $KL = KM$. The triangle is an isosceles triangle, therefore $m\angle L = m\angle M = 3x + 5$.

$m\angle L + m\angle M + m\angle K = 180$ Angle Sum Theorem

$(3x + 5) + (3x + 5) + (5x + 5) = 180$ Substitution

$11x + 15 = 180$ Simplify.

$11x = 165$ Subtract 15 from each side.

$x = 15$ Divide each side by 11.

So, $m\angle K = 5(15) + 5 = 80$.

Exercises

ALGEBRA Find each measure.

1. x **39**

2. $m\angle W$ **51**

3. x **16**

4. $m\angle T$ **58**

5. $m\angle R$ **105**

6. $m\angle S$ **70**

7. $m\angle W$ **72**

8. $m\angle X$ **86**

NAME _____ DATE _____ PERIOD _____

10-4 Skills Practice

Inscribed Angles

Find each measure.

1. $m\,\widehat{XY}$ **46**

2. $m\angle E$ **81**

3. $m\angle R$ **50**

4. $m\,\widehat{MP}$ **118**

ALGEBRA Find each measure.

5. $m\angle N$ **17**

6. $m\angle L$ **54**

7. $m\angle C$ **43**

8. $m\angle A$ **89**

9. $m\angle J$ **58**

10. $m\angle K$ **32**

11. $m\angle S$ **95**

12. $m\angle R$ **110**

Answers

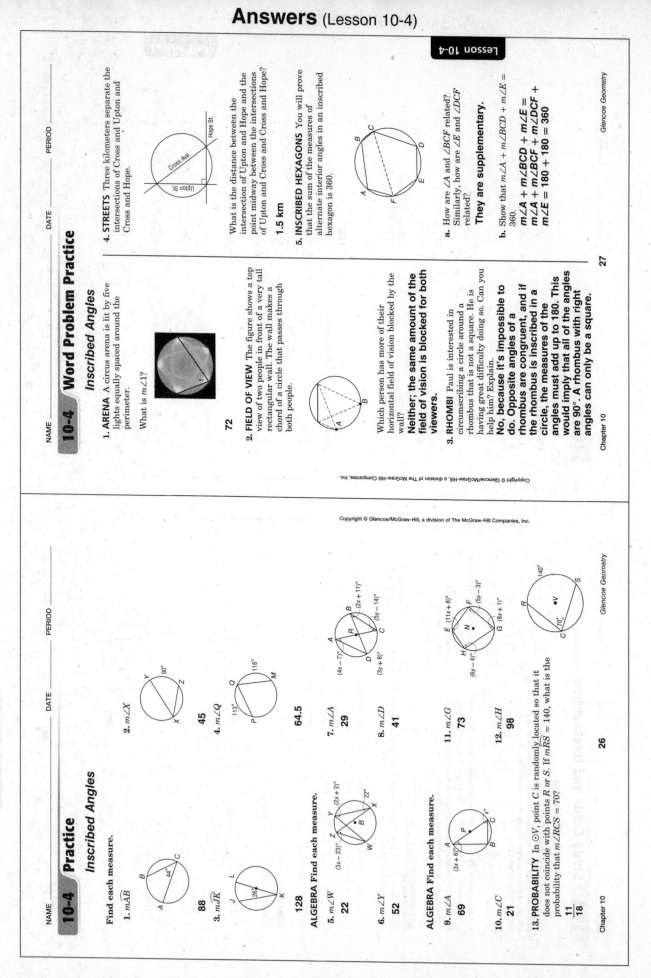

NAME _____ DATE _____ PERIOD _____

10-4 Practice

Inscribed Angles

Find each measure.

1. $m\widehat{AB}$

88

2. $m\angle X$

45

3. $m\widehat{JK}$

128

4. $m\angle Q$

64.5

ALGEBRA Find each measure.

5. $m\angle W$

22

6. $m\angle Y$

52

7. $m\angle A$

29

8. $m\angle D$

41

ALGEBRA Find each measure.

9. $m\angle A$

69

10. $m\angle C$

21

11. $m\angle G$

73

12. $m\angle H$

98

13. **PROBABILITY** In $\odot V$, point C is randomly located so that it does not coincide with points R or S. If $m\widehat{RS} = 140$, what is the probability that $m\angle RCS = 70$?

$\dfrac{11}{18}$

Chapter 10   26   Glencoe Geometry

NAME _____ DATE _____ PERIOD _____

10-4 Word Problem Practice

Inscribed Angles

1. **ARENA** A circus arena is lit by five lights equally spaced around the perimeter.

   What is $m\angle 1$?

   72

2. **FIELD OF VIEW** The figure shows a top view of two people in front of a very tall rectangular wall. The wall makes a chord of a circle that passes through both people.

   Which person has more of their horizontal field of vision blocked by the wall?

   Neither; the same amount of the field of vision is blocked for both viewers.

3. **RHOMBI** Paul is interested in circumscribing a circle around a rhombus that is not a square. He is having great difficulty doing so. Can you help him? Explain.

   No, because it's impossible to do. Opposite angles of a rhombus are congruent, and if the rhombus is inscribed in a circle, the measures of the angles must add up to 180. This would imply that all of the angles are 90°. A rhombus with right angles can only be a square.

4. **STREETS** Three kilometers separate the intersections of Cross and Upton and Cross and Hope.

   What is the distance between the intersection of Upton and Hope and the point midway between the intersections of Upton and Cross and Cross and Hope?

   1.5 km

5. **INSCRIBED HEXAGONS** You will prove that the sum of the measures of alternate interior angles in an inscribed hexagon is 360.

   a. How are $\angle A$ and $\angle BCF$ related? Similarly, how are $\angle E$ and $\angle DCF$ related?

   They are supplementary.

   b. Show that $m\angle A + m\angle BCD + m\angle E = 360$.

   $m\angle A + m\angle BCD + m\angle E = m\angle A + m\angle BCF + m\angle DCF + m\angle E = 180 + 180 = 360$

Chapter 10   27   Glencoe Geometry

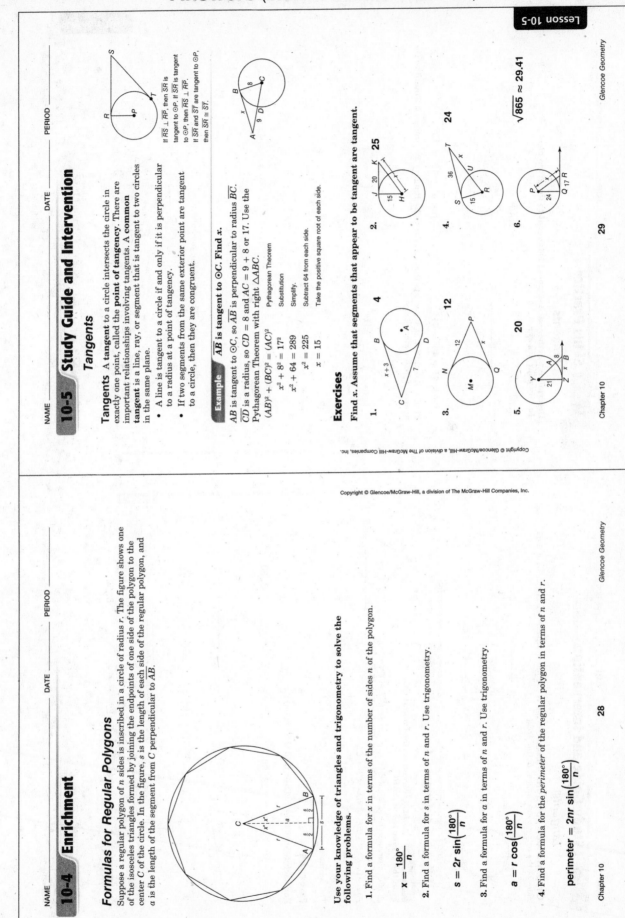

NAME _____ DATE _____ PERIOD _____

10-4 Enrichment

Formulas for Regular Polygons

Suppose a regular polygon of n sides is inscribed in a circle of radius r. The figure shows one of the isosceles triangles formed by joining the endpoints of one side of the polygon to the center C of the circle. In the figure, s is the length of each side of the regular polygon, and a is the length of the segment from C perpendicular to $\overline{AB}$.

Use your knowledge of triangles and trigonometry to solve the following problems.

1. Find a formula for x in terms of the number of sides n of the polygon.

$$x = \frac{180°}{n}$$

2. Find a formula for s in terms of n and r. Use trigonometry.

$$s = 2r\sin\left(\frac{180°}{n}\right)$$

3. Find a formula for a in terms of n and r. Use trigonometry.

$$a = r\cos\left(\frac{180°}{n}\right)$$

4. Find a formula for the *perimeter* of the regular polygon in terms of n and r.

$$\text{perimeter} = 2nr\sin\left(\frac{180°}{n}\right)$$

Chapter 10   28   *Glencoe Geometry*

NAME _____ DATE _____ PERIOD _____

10-5 Study Guide and Intervention

Tangents

Tangents A **tangent** to a circle intersects the circle in exactly one point, called the **point of tangency**. There are important relationships involving tangents. A **common tangent** is a line, ray, or segment that is tangent to two circles in the same plane.

- A line is tangent to a circle if and only if it is perpendicular to a radius at a point of tangency.
- If two segments from the same exterior point are tangent to a circle, then they are congruent.

If $\overline{RS} \perp \overline{RP}$, then $\overline{SR}$ is tangent to $\odot P$. If $\overline{SR}$ is tangent to $\odot P$, then $\overline{RS} \perp \overline{RP}$.

If $\overline{SR}$ and $\overline{ST}$ are tangent to $\odot P$, then $\overline{SR} \cong \overline{ST}$.

Example $\overline{AB}$ **is tangent to** $\odot C$. **Find x.**

$\overline{AB}$ is tangent to $\odot C$, so $\overline{AB}$ is perpendicular to radius $\overline{BC}$. $\overline{CD}$ is a radius, so $CD = 8$ and $AC = 9 + 8$ or 17. Use the Pythagorean Theorem with right $\triangle ABC$.

$(AB)^2 + (BC)^2 = (AC)^2$	Pythagorean Theorem
$x^2 + 8^2 = 17^2$	Substitution
$x^2 + 64 = 289$	Simplify.
$x^2 = 225$	Subtract 64 from each side.
$x = 15$	Take the positive square root of each side.

Exercises

Find x. Assume that segments that appear to be tangent are tangent.

1. **4**

2. **25**

3. **12**

4. **24**

5. **20**

6. $\sqrt{865} \approx 29.41$

Chapter 10   29   *Glencoe Geometry*

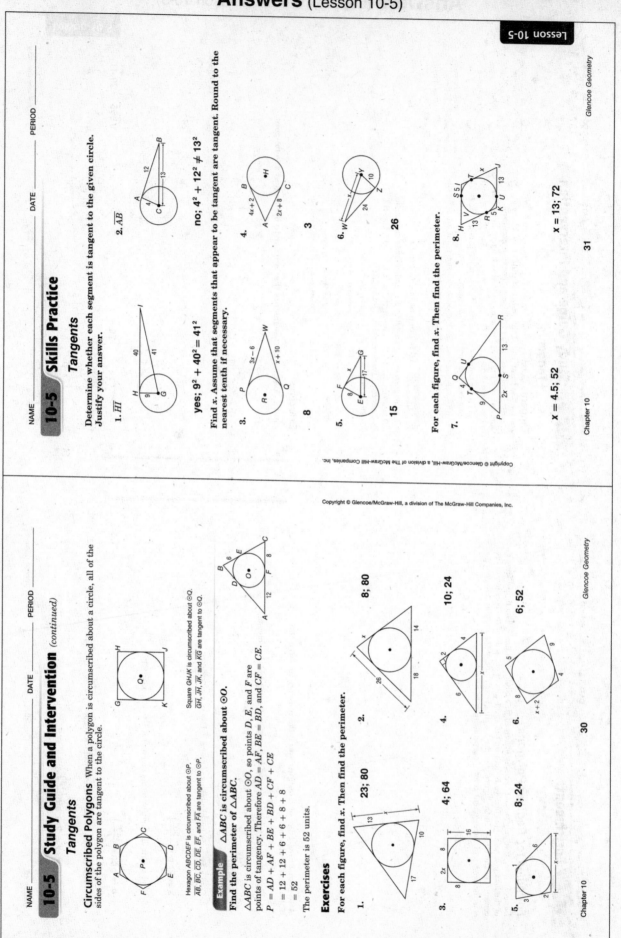

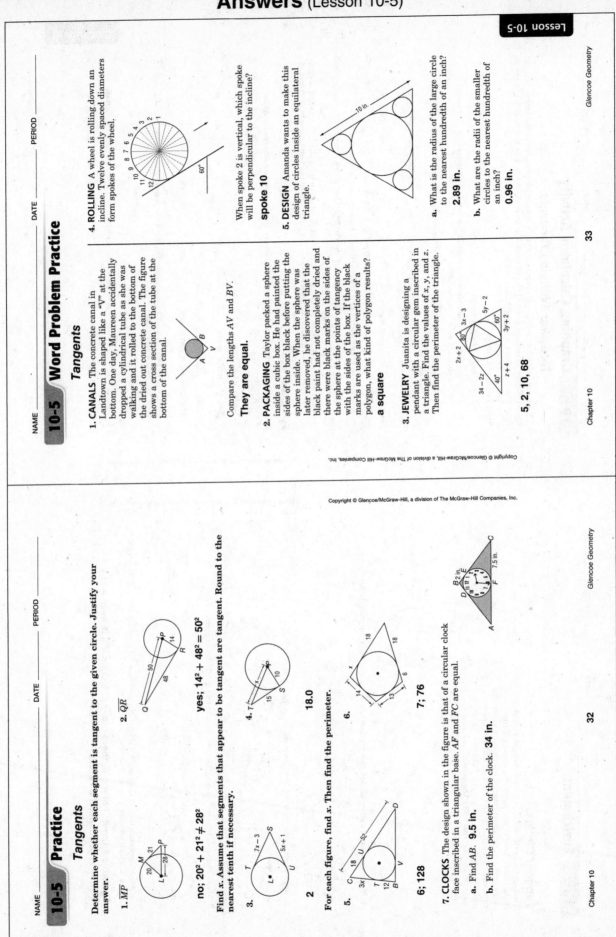

NAME _____ DATE _____ PERIOD _____

10-5 Practice

Tangents

Determine whether each segment is tangent to the given circle. Justify your answer.

1. $\overline{MP}$

no; $20^2 + 21^2 \neq 28^2$

2. $\overline{QR}$

yes; $14^2 + 48^2 = 50^2$

Find x. Assume that segments that appear to be tangent are tangent. Round to the nearest tenth if necessary.

3.

2

4.

18.0

For each figure, find x. Then find the perimeter.

5.

6; 128

6.

7; 76

7. **CLOCKS** The design shown in the figure is that of a circular clock face inscribed in a triangular base. AF and FC are equal.

a. Find AB. **9.5 in.**

b. Find the perimeter of the clock. **34 in.**

Chapter 10   32   Glencoe Geometry

NAME _____ DATE _____ PERIOD _____

10-5 Word Problem Practice

Tangents

1. **CANALS** The concrete canal in Landtown is shaped like a "V" at the bottom. One day, Maureen accidentally dropped a cylindrical tube as she was walking and it rolled to the bottom of the dried out concrete canal. The figure shows a cross section of the tube at the bottom of the canal.

Compare the lengths AV and BV.

They are equal.

2. **PACKAGING** Taylor packed a sphere inside a cubic box. He had painted the sides of the box black before putting the sphere inside. When the sphere was later removed, he discovered that the black paint had not completely dried and there were black marks on the sides of the sphere at the points of tangency with the sides of the box. If the black marks are used as the vertices of a polygon, what kind of polygon results?

a square

3. **JEWELRY** Juanita is designing a pendant with a circular gem inscribed in a triangle. Find the values of x, y, and z. Then find the perimeter of the triangle.

5, 2, 10, 68

4. **ROLLING** A wheel is rolling down an incline. Twelve evenly spaced diameters form spokes of the wheel.

When spoke 2 is vertical, which spoke will be perpendicular to the incline?

spoke 10

5. **DESIGN** Amanda wants to make this design of circles inside an equilateral triangle.

a. What is the radius of the large circle to the nearest hundredth of an inch?

2.89 in.

b. What are the radii of the smaller circles to the nearest hundredth of an inch?

0.96 in.

Chapter 10   33   Glencoe Geometry

NAME _____ DATE _____ PERIOD _____

10-5 Graphing Calculator Activity

TI-Nspire: Exploring Tangents

A line that intersects a circle in exactly one point is called a **tangent** to the circle. You can use TI-Nspire to explore some of the characteristics of tangents. Use the following steps to draw two lines that are tangent to a circle.

Step 1 Draw a circle.

- From the **8: Shapes** menu select **1: Circle**.
- Place the cursor on the left center part of the screen and press ⏎. You have established the center of the circle.
- Press the left arrow to increase the radius length of the circle. Press ⏎ when the circle has a desirable radius.
- From the **1: Actions** menu select **5: Text**. Press ⏎ near the center of the circle and label the center of the circle C.

Step 2 Draw a tangent line.

- From the **6: Points and Lines** menu select **7: Tangent**.
- Move the cursor to the circle. Press ⏎. A tangent line is now drawn.
- Move the cursor to another point on the circle so that a new tangent line appears and intersects the first tangent line. Press ⏎.
- From the **1: Actions** menu use the **5: Text** function to label the first point of tangency T, the second point of tangency, S and the point where the two tangents intersect, A.

Exercises

Use the measuring capabilities of TI-Nspire to explore the characteristics of tangents.

1. Measure the lengths of $\overline{AT}$ and $\overline{AS}$.

   See students' work.

2. Make a conjecture about AT and AS.

   The measures are equal.

3. From the **6: Points and Lines** menu use the **5: Segment** tool to draw radii $\overline{CT}$ and $\overline{CS}$. Measure ∠CTA and ∠CSA.

   See students' work.

4. Make a conjecture about the angles formed by a radius and a tangent to a circle.

   They are right angles.

Chapter 10   35   Glencoe Geometry

NAME _____ DATE _____ PERIOD _____

10-5 Enrichment

Tangent Circles

Two circles in the same plane are **tangent circles** if they have exactly one point in common. Tangent circles with no common interior points are **externally tangent**. If tangent circles have common interior points, then they are **internally tangent**. Three or more circles are **mutually tangent** if each pair of them is tangent.

Externally Tangent Circles

Internally Tangent Circles

1. Make sketches to show all possible positions of three mutually tangent circles.

2. Make sketches to show all possible positions of four mutually tangent circles.

3. Make sketches to show all possible positions of five mutually tangent circles.

4. Write a conjecture about the number of possible positions for n mutually tangent circles if n is a whole number greater than four.

   Possible answer: For $n > 4$, there are $\frac{n}{2}$ positions if n is even and $\frac{1}{2}(n + 1)$ positions if n is odd.

Chapter 10   34   Glencoe Geometry

Answers (Lesson 10-5 and Lesson 10-6)

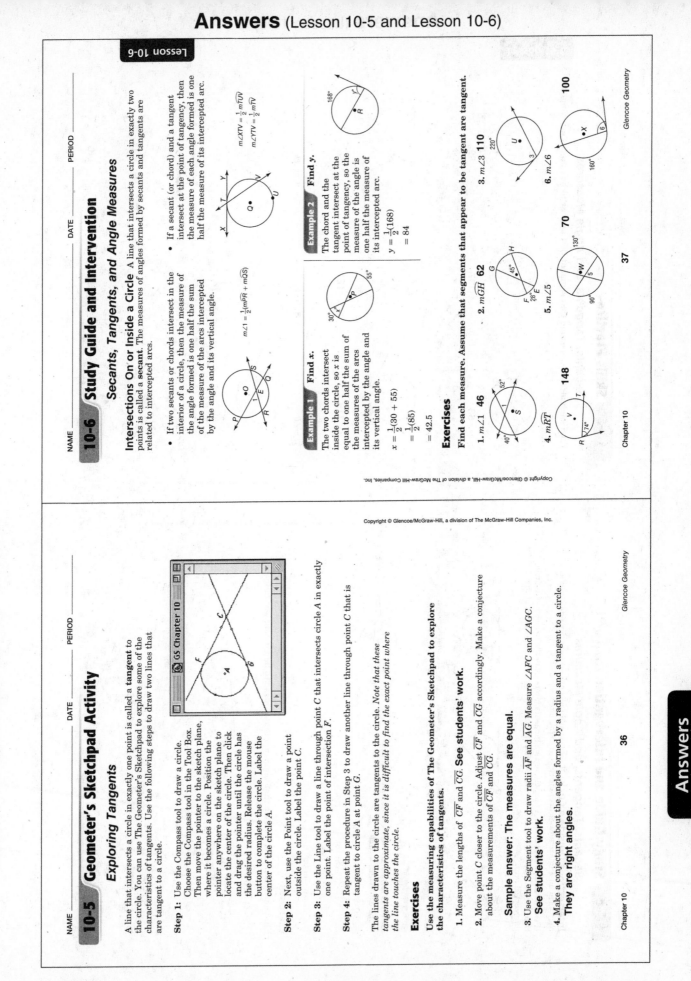

NAME ___ DATE ___ PERIOD ___

10-5 Geometer's Sketchpad Activity

Exploring Tangents

A line that intersects a circle in exactly one point is called a **tangent** to the circle. You can use The Geometer's Sketchpad to explore some of the characteristics of tangents. Use the following steps to draw two lines that are tangent to a circle.

Step 1: Use the Compass tool to draw a circle. Choose the Compass tool in the Tool Box. Then move the pointer to the sketch plane, where it becomes a circle. Position the pointer anywhere on the sketch plane to locate the center of the circle. Then click and drag the pointer until the circle has the desired radius. Release the mouse button to complete the circle. Label the center of the circle A.

Step 2: Next, use the Point tool to draw a point outside the circle. Label the point C.

Step 3: Use the Line tool to draw a line through point C that intersects circle A in exactly one point. Label the point of intersection F.

Step 4: Repeat the procedure in Step 3 to draw another line through point C that is tangent to circle A at point G.

The lines drawn through the circle are tangents to the circle. *Note that these tangents are approximate, since it is difficult to find the exact point where the line touches the circle.*

Exercises

Use the measuring capabilities of The Geometer's Sketchpad to explore the characteristics of tangents.

1. Measure the lengths of $\overline{CF}$ and $\overline{CG}$. **See students' work.**

2. Move point C closer to the circle. Adjust $\overline{CF}$ and $\overline{CG}$ accordingly. Make a conjecture about the measurements of $\overline{CF}$ and $\overline{CG}$.
Sample answer: The measures are equal.

3. Use the Segment tool to draw radii $\overline{AF}$ and $\overline{AG}$. Measure $\angle AFC$ and $\angle AGC$. **See students' work.**

4. Make a conjecture about the angles formed by a radius and a tangent to a circle. **They are right angles.**

Chapter 10   36   *Glencoe Geometry*

NAME ___ DATE ___ PERIOD ___

10-6 Study Guide and Intervention
Secants, Tangents, and Angle Measures

Intersections On or Inside a Circle A line that intersects a circle in exactly two points is called a **secant**. The measures of angles formed by secants and tangents are related to intercepted arcs.

- If two secants or chords intersect in the interior of a circle, then the measure of the angle formed is one half the sum of the measure of the arcs intercepted by the angle and its vertical angle.

$$m\angle 1 = \tfrac{1}{2}(m\overset{\frown}{PR} + m\overset{\frown}{QS})$$

- If a secant (or chord) and a tangent intersect at the point of tangency, then the measure of each angle formed is one half the measure of its intercepted arc.

$$m\angle YTV = \tfrac{1}{2}m\overset{\frown}{TUV}$$
$$m\angle YTV = \tfrac{1}{2}m\overset{\frown}{TV}$$

Example 1 Find x.

The two chords intersect inside the circle, so x is equal to one half the sum of the measures of the arcs intercepted by the angle and its vertical angle.

$$x = \tfrac{1}{2}(30 + 55)$$
$$= \tfrac{1}{2}(85)$$
$$= 42.5$$

Example 2 Find y.

The chord and the tangent intersect at the point of tangency, so the measure of the angle is one half the measure of its intercepted arc.

$$y = \tfrac{1}{2}(168)$$
$$= 84$$

Exercises

Find each measure. Assume that segments that appear to be tangent are tangent.

1. $m\angle 1$ **46**

2. $m\overset{\frown}{GH}$ **62**

3. $m\angle 3$ **110**

4. $m\overset{\frown}{RT}$ **148**

5. $m\angle 5$ **70**

6. $m\angle 6$ **100**

37

Chapter 10   **A17**   *Glencoe Geometry*

Answers

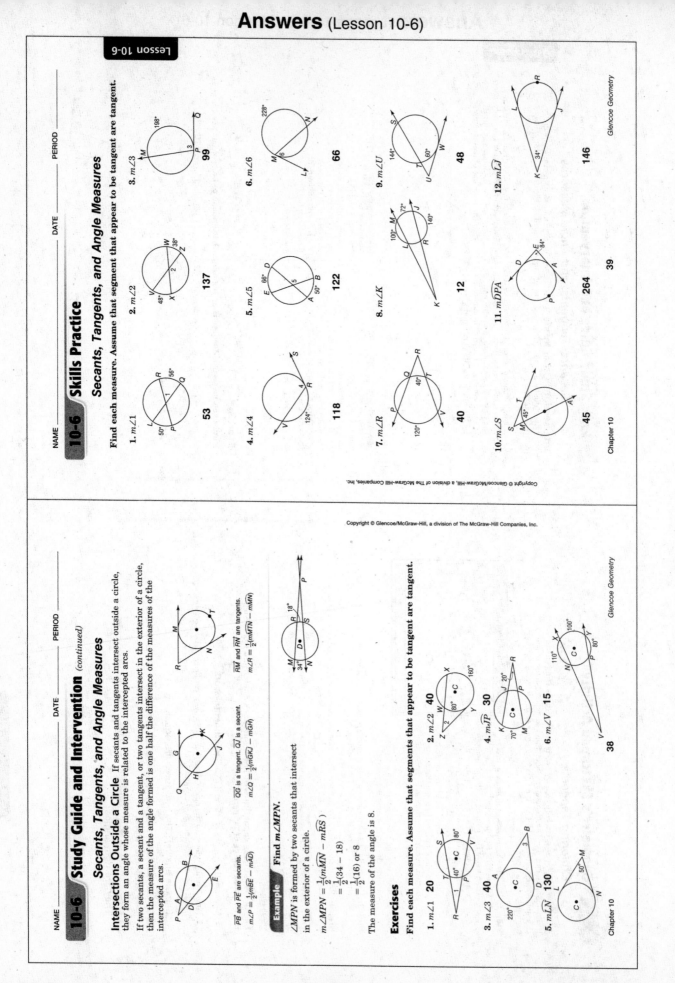

NAME _____ DATE _____ PERIOD _____

10-6 Skills Practice

Secants, Tangents, and Angle Measures

Find each measure. Assume that segment that appear to be tangent are tangent.

1. m∠1   53
2. m∠2   137
3. m∠3   99

4. m∠4   118
5. m∠5   122
6. m∠6   66

7. m∠R   40
8. m∠K   12
9. m∠U   48

10. m∠S   45
11. mDPA   264
12. mLJ   146

Chapter 10

Glencoe Geometry

NAME _____ DATE _____ PERIOD _____

10-6 Study Guide and Intervention (continued)

Secants, Tangents, and Angle Measures

Intersections Outside a Circle If secants and tangents intersect outside a circle, they form an angle whose measure is related to the intercepted arcs.

If two secants, a secant and a tangent, or two tangents intersect in the exterior of a circle, then the measure of the angle formed is one half the difference of the measures of the intercepted arcs.

$\overline{PB}$ and $\overline{PE}$ are secants.

$m\angle P = \frac{1}{2}(m\widehat{BE} - m\widehat{AD})$

$\overline{QG}$ is a tangent. $\overline{QJ}$ is a secant.

$m\angle Q = \frac{1}{2}(m\widehat{GKJ} - m\widehat{GH})$

$\overline{RM}$ and $\overline{RN}$ are tangents.

$m\angle R = \frac{1}{2}(m\widehat{MTN} - m\widehat{MN})$

Example Find m∠MPN.

∠MPN is formed by two secants that intersect in the exterior of a circle.

$m\angle MPN = \frac{1}{2}(m\widehat{MN} - m\widehat{RS})$

$= \frac{1}{2}(34 - 18)$

$= \frac{1}{2}(16)$ or 8

The measure of the angle is 8.

Exercises

Find each measure. Assume that segments that appear to be tangent are tangent.

1. m∠1   20
2. m∠2   40
3. m∠3   40
4. mJP   30
5. mLN   130
6. m∠V   15

Chapter 10

Glencoe Geometry

NAME _____ DATE _____ PERIOD _____

10-6 Practice

Secants, Tangents, and Angle Measures

Find each measure. Assume that any segments that appear to be tangent are tangent.

1. $m\angle 1$

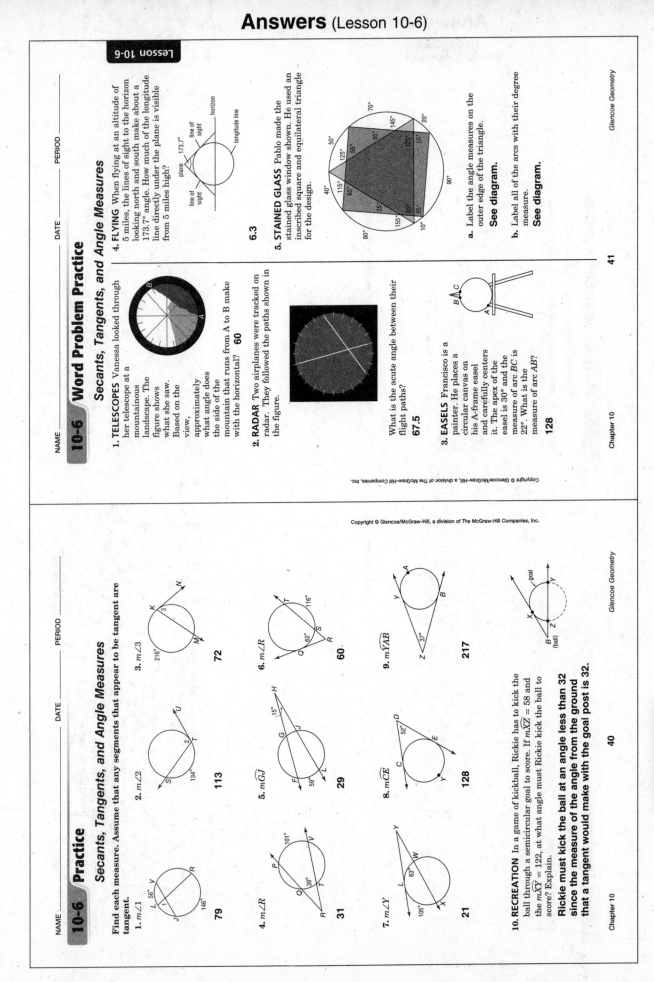

79

2. $m\angle 2$

113

3. $m\angle 3$

72

4. $m\angle R$

31

5. $m\widehat{GJ}$

29

6. $m\angle R$

60

7. $m\angle Y$

21

8. $m\widehat{CE}$

128

9. $m\widehat{YAB}$

217

10. RECREATION In a game of kickball, Rickie has to kick the ball through a semicircular goal to score. If $m\widehat{XZ} = 58$ and the $m\widehat{XY} = 122$, at what angle must Rickie kick the ball to score? Explain.

Rickie must kick the ball at an angle less than 32 since the measure of the angle from the ground that a tangent would make with the goal post is 32.

NAME _____ DATE _____ PERIOD _____

10-6 Word Problem Practice

Secants, Tangents, and Angle Measures

1. TELESCOPES Vanessa looked through her telescope at a mountainous landscape. The figure shows what she saw. Based on the view, approximately what angle does the side of the mountain that runs from A to B make with the horizontal? **60**

2. RADAR Two airplanes were tracked on radar. They followed the paths shown in the figure.

What is the acute angle between their flight paths? **67.5**

3. EASELS Francisco is a painter. He places a circular canvas on his A-frame easel and carefully centers it. The apex of the easel is 30° and the measure of arc BC is 22°. What is the measure of arc AB? **128**

4. FLYING When flying at an altitude of 5 miles, the lines of sight to the horizon looking north and south make about a 173.7° angle. How much of the longitude line directly under the plane is visible from 5 miles high? **6.3**

5. STAINED GLASS Pablo made the stained glass window shown. He used an inscribed square and equilateral triangle for the design.

a. Label the angle measures on the outer edge of the triangle. **See diagram.**

b. Label all of the arcs with their degree measure. **See diagram.**

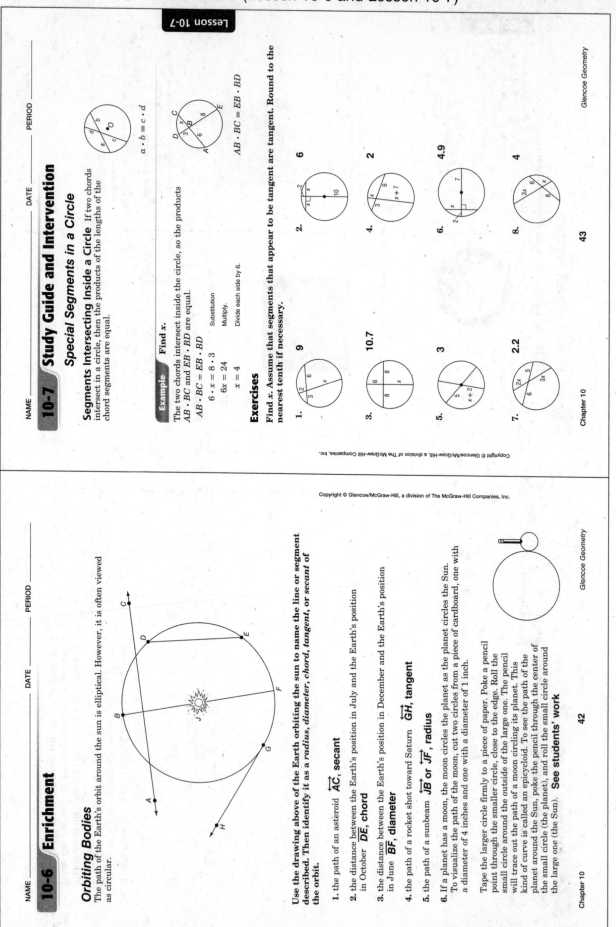

NAME _____ DATE _____ PERIOD _____

10-7 Study Guide and Intervention

Special Segments in a Circle

Segments Intersecting Inside a Circle If two chords intersect in a circle, then the products of the lengths of the chord segments are equal.

$a \cdot b = c \cdot d$

Example **Find x.**

The two chords intersect inside the circle, so the products $AB \cdot BC$ and $EB \cdot BD$ are equal.

$AB \cdot BC = EB \cdot BD$
$6 \cdot x = 8 \cdot 3$ Substitution
$6x = 24$ Multiply.
$x = 4$ Divide each side by 6.

$AB \cdot BC = EB \cdot BD$

Exercises

Find x. Assume that segments that appear to be tangent are tangent. Round to the nearest tenth if necessary.

1. **9**
2. **6**
3. **10.7**
4. **2**
5. **3**
6. **4.9**
7. **2.2**
8. **4**

Chapter 10   43   Glencoe Geometry

NAME _____ DATE _____ PERIOD _____

10-6 Enrichment

Orbiting Bodies

The path of the Earth's orbit around the sun is elliptical. However, it is often viewed as circular.

Use the drawing above of the Earth orbiting the sun to name the line or segment described. Then identify it as a *radius, diameter, chord, tangent,* or *secant* of the orbit.

1. the path of an asteroid $\overleftrightarrow{AC}$, **secant**

2. the distance between the Earth's position in July and the Earth's position in October $\overline{DE}$, **chord**

3. the distance between the Earth's position in December and the Earth's position in June $\overline{BF}$, **diameter**

4. the path of a rocket shot toward Saturn $\overleftrightarrow{GH}$, **tangent**

5. the path of a sunbeam $\overrightarrow{JB}$ or $\overrightarrow{JF}$, **radius**

6. If a planet has a moon, the moon circles the planet as the planet circles the Sun. To visualize the path of the moon, cut two circles from a piece of cardboard, one with a diameter of 4 inches and one with a diameter of 1 inch.

Tape the larger circle firmly to a piece of paper. Poke a pencil point through the smaller circle, close to the edge. Roll the small circle around the outside of the large one. The pencil will trace out the path of a moon circling its planet. This kind of curve is called an epicycloid. To see the path of the planet around the Sun, poke the pencil through the center of the small circle (the planet), and roll the small circle around the large one (the Sun). **See students' work**

Chapter 10   42   Glencoe Geometry

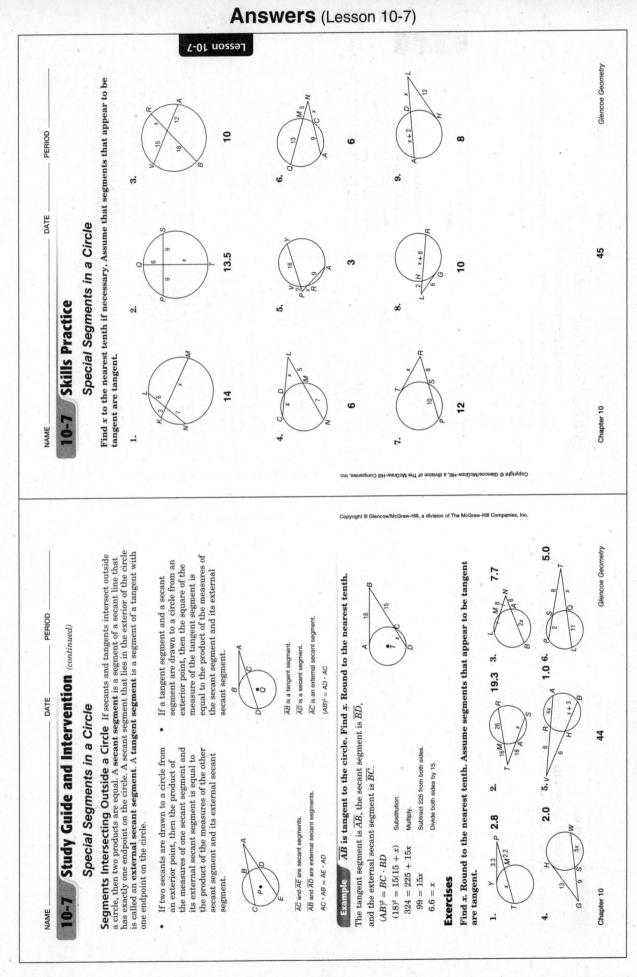

Answers (Lesson 10-7)

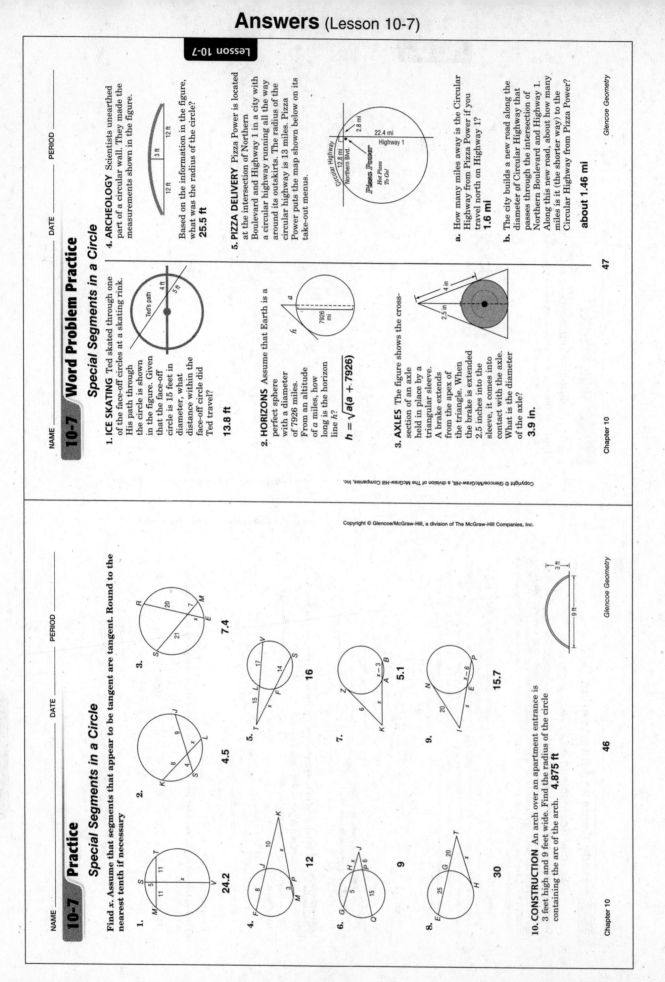

Page 46 (left side)

10-7 Practice

Special Segments in a Circle

Find *x*. Assume that segments that appear to be tangent are tangent. Round to the nearest tenth if necessary.

1. **24.2**

2. **4.5**

3. **7.4**

4. **12**

5. **16**

6. **9**

7. **5.1**

8. **30**

9. **15.7**

10. **CONSTRUCTION** An arch over an apartment entrance is 3 feet high and 9 feet wide. Find the radius of the circle containing the arc of the arch. **4.875 ft**

Page 47 (right side)

10-7 Word Problem Practice

Special Segments in a Circle

1. **ICE SKATING** Ted skated through one of the face-off circles at a skating rink. His path through the circle is shown in the figure. Given that the face-off circle is 15 feet in diameter, what distance within the face-off circle did Ted travel?

13.8 ft

2. **HORIZONS** Assume that Earth is a perfect sphere with a diameter of 7926 miles. From an altitude of *a* miles, how long is the horizon line *h*?

$$h = \sqrt{a(a + 7926)}$$

3. **AXLES** The figure shows the cross-section of an axle held in place by a triangular sleeve. A brake extends from the apex of the triangle. When the brake is extended 2.5 inches into the sleeve, it comes into contact with the axle. What is the diameter of the axle?

3.9 in.

4. **ARCHEOLOGY** Scientists unearthed part of a circular wall. They made the measurements shown in the figure.

Based on the information in the figure, what was the radius of the circle? **25.5 ft**

5. **PIZZA DELIVERY** Pizza Power is located at the intersection of Northern Boulevard and Highway 1 in a city with a circular highway running all the way around its outskirts. The radius of the circular highway is 13 miles. Pizza Power puts the map shown below on its take-out menus.

a. How many miles away is the Circular Highway from Pizza Power if you travel north on Highway 1? **1.6 mi**

b. The city builds a new road along the diameter of Circular Highway that passes through the intersection of Northern Boulevard and Highway 1. Along this new road, about how many miles is it (the shorter way) to the Circular Highway from Pizza Power? **about 1.46 mi**

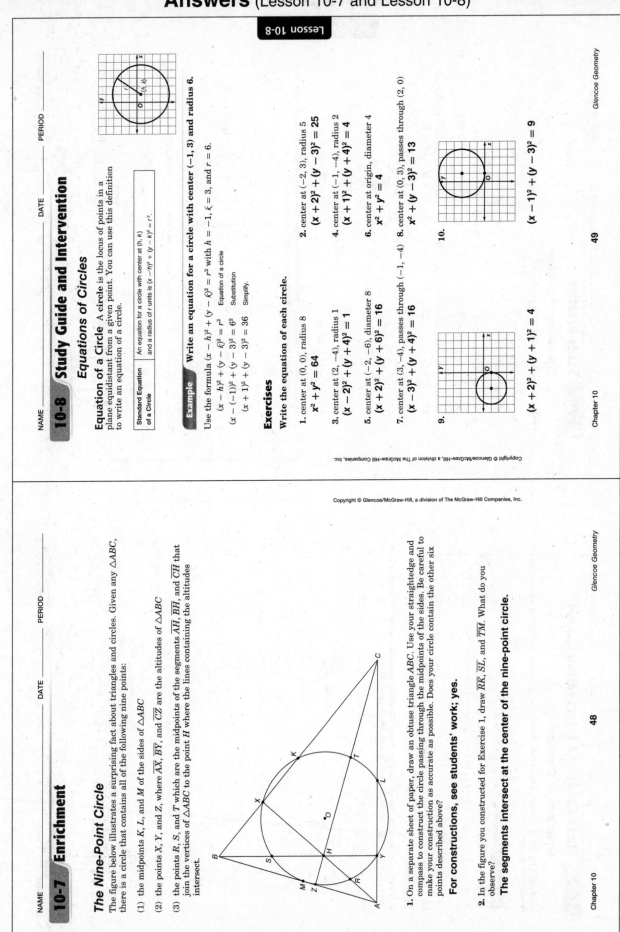

NAME _____ DATE _____ PERIOD _____

10-7 Enrichment

The Nine-Point Circle

The figure below illustrates a surprising fact about triangles and circles. Given any △ABC, there is a circle that contains all of the following nine points:

(1) the midpoints K, L, and M of the sides of △ABC

(2) the points X, Y, and Z, where $\overline{AX}$, $\overline{BY}$, and $\overline{CZ}$ are the altitudes of △ABC

(3) the points R, S, and T which are the midpoints of the segments $\overline{AH}$, $\overline{BH}$, and $\overline{CH}$ that join the vertices of △ABC to the point H where the lines containing the altitudes intersect.

1. On a separate sheet of paper, draw an obtuse triangle ABC. Use your straightedge and compass to construct the circle passing through the midpoints of the sides. Be careful to make your construction as accurate as possible. Does your circle contain the other six points described above?

For constructions, see students' work; yes.

2. In the figure you constructed for Exercise 1, draw $\overline{RK}$, $\overline{SL}$, and $\overline{TM}$. What do you observe?

The segments intersect at the center of the nine-point circle.

NAME _____ DATE _____ PERIOD _____

10-8 Study Guide and Intervention

Equations of Circles

Equation of a Circle A circle is the locus of points in a plane equidistant from a given point. You can use this definition to write an equation of a circle.

Standard Equation of a Circle	An equation for a circle with center at (h, k) and a radius of r units is $(x - h)^2 + (y - k)^2 = r^2$.

Example Write an equation for a circle with center $(-1, 3)$ and radius 6.

Use the formula $(x - h)^2 + (y - k)^2 = r^2$ with $h = -1$, $k = 3$, and $r = 6$.

$(x - h)^2 + (y - k)^2 = r^2$ Equation of a circle

$(x - (-1))^2 + (y - 3)^2 = 6^2$ Substitution

$(x + 1)^2 + (y - 3)^2 = 36$ Simplify.

Exercises

Write the equation of each circle.

1. center at $(0, 0)$, radius 8
$x^2 + y^2 = 64$

2. center at $(-2, 3)$, radius 5
$(x + 2)^2 + (y - 3)^2 = 25$

3. center at $(2, -4)$, radius 1
$(x - 2)^2 + (y + 4)^2 = 1$

4. center at $(-1, -4)$, radius 2
$(x + 1)^2 + (y + 4)^2 = 4$

5. center at $(-2, -6)$, diameter 8
$(x + 2)^2 + (y + 6)^2 = 16$

6. center at origin, diameter 4
$x^2 + y^2 = 4$

7. center at $(3, -4)$, passes through $(-1, -4)$
$(x - 3)^2 + (y + 4)^2 = 16$

8. center at $(0, 3)$, passes through $(2, 0)$
$x^2 + (y - 3)^2 = 13$

9.
$(x + 2)^2 + (y + 1)^2 = 4$

10.
$(x - 1)^2 + (y - 3)^2 = 9$

Answers

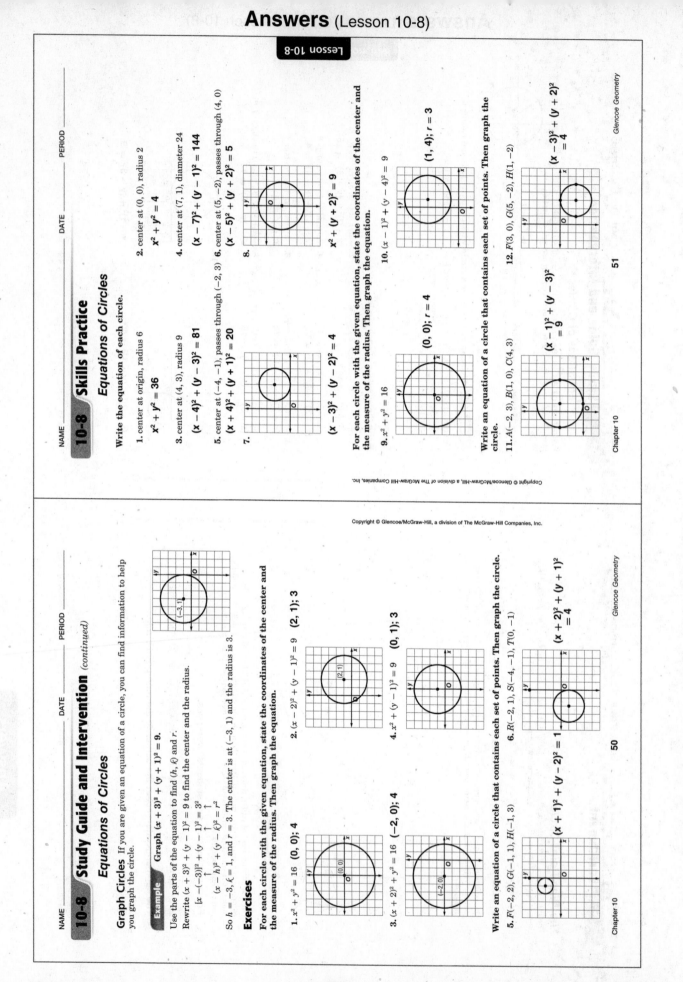

10-8 Skills Practice

Equations of Circles

Write the equation of each circle.

1. center at origin, radius 6

$x^2 + y^2 = 36$

2. center at $(0, 0)$, radius 2

$x^2 + y^2 = 4$

3. center at $(4, 3)$, radius 9

$(x - 4)^2 + (y - 3)^2 = 81$

4. center at $(7, 1)$, diameter 24

$(x - 7)^2 + (y - 1)^2 = 144$

5. center at $(-4, -1)$, passes through $(-2, 3)$

$(x + 4)^2 + (y + 1)^2 = 20$

6. center at $(5, -2)$, passes through $(4, 0)$

$(x - 5)^2 + (y + 2)^2 = 5$

7.

$(x - 3)^2 + (y - 2)^2 = 4$

8.

$x^2 + (y + 2)^2 = 9$

For each circle with the given equation, state the coordinates of the center and the measure of the radius. Then graph the equation.

9. $x^2 + y^2 = 16$

$(0, 0); r = 4$

10. $(x - 1)^2 + (y - 4)^2 = 9$

$(1, 4); r = 3$

Write an equation of a circle that contains each set of points. Then graph the circle.

11. $A(-2, 3), B(1, 0), C(4, 3)$

$(x - 1)^2 + (y - 3)^2 = 9$

12. $F(3, 0), G(5, -2), H(1, -2)$

$(x - 3)^2 + (y + 2)^2 = 4$

10-8 Study Guide and Intervention (continued)

Equations of Circles

Graph Circles If you are given an equation of a circle, you can find information to help you graph the circle.

Example Graph $(x + 3)^2 + (y + 1)^2 = 9$.

Use the parts of the equation to find (h, k) and r.

Rewrite $(x + 3)^2 + (y - 1)^2 = 9$ to find the center and the radius.

$[x - (-3)]^2 + (y - 1)^2 = 3^2$

$(x - h)^2 + (y - k)^2 = r^2$

So $h = -3, k = 1$, and $r = 3$. The center is at $(-3, 1)$ and the radius is 3.

Exercises

For each circle with the given equation, state the coordinates of the center and the measure of the radius. Then graph the equation.

1. $x^2 + y^2 = 16$ $(0, 0); 4$

2. $(x - 2)^2 + (y - 1)^2 = 9$ $(2, 1); 3$

3. $(x + 2)^2 + y^2 = 16$ $(-2, 0); 4$

4. $x^2 + (y - 1)^2 = 9$ $(0, 1); 3$

Write an equation of a circle that contains each set of points. Then graph the circle.

5. $F(-2, 2), G(-1, 1), H(-1, 3)$

$(x + 1)^2 + (y - 2)^2 = 1$

6. $R(-2, 1), S(-4, -1), T(0, -1)$

$(x + 2)^2 + (y + 1)^2 = 4$

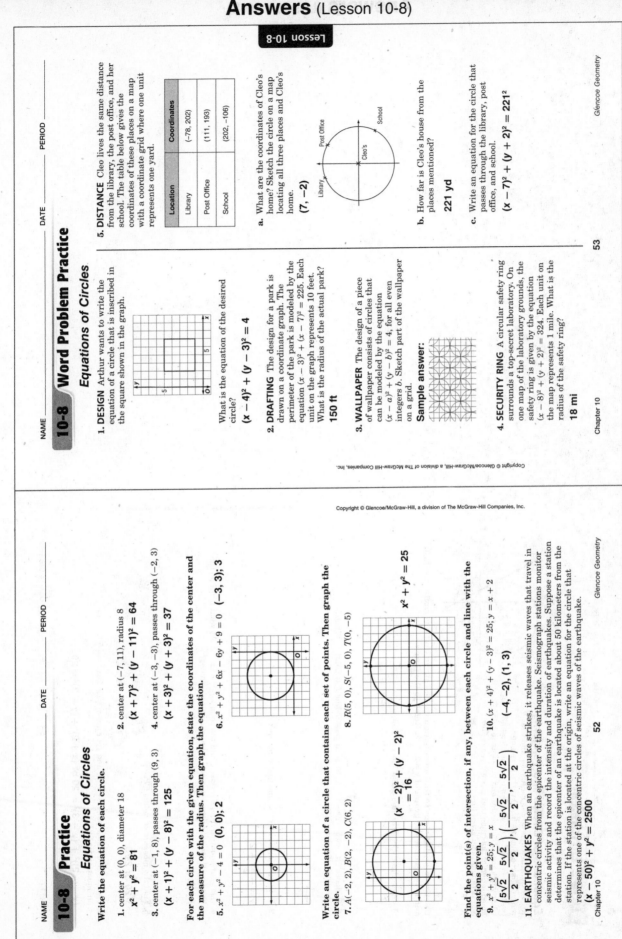

NAME _____ DATE _____ PERIOD _____

10-8 Practice

Equations of Circles

Write the equation of each circle.

1. center at (0, 0), diameter 18
   $x^2 + y^2 = 81$

2. center at (−7, 11), radius 8
   $(x + 7)^2 + (y − 11)^2 = 64$

3. center at (−1, 8), passes through (9, 3)
   $(x + 1)^2 + (y − 8)^2 = 125$

4. center at (−3, −3), passes through (−2, 3)
   $(x + 3)^2 + (y + 3)^2 = 37$

For each circle with the given equation, state the coordinates of the center and the measure of the radius. Then graph the equation.

5. $x^2 + y^2 − 4 = 0$ (0, 0); 2

6. $x^2 + y^2 + 6x − 6y + 9 = 0$ (−3, 3); 3

Write an equation of a circle that contains each set of points. Then graph the circle.

7. A(−2, 2), B(2, −2), C(6, 2)
   $(x − 2)^2 + (y − 2)^2 = 16$

8. R(5, 0), S(−5, 0), T(0, −5)
   $x^2 + y^2 = 25$

Find the point(s) of intersection, if any, between each circle and line with the equations given.

9. $x^2 + y^2 = 25; y = x$
   $\left(\dfrac{5\sqrt{2}}{2}, \dfrac{5\sqrt{2}}{2}\right), \left(−\dfrac{5\sqrt{2}}{2}, −\dfrac{5\sqrt{2}}{2}\right)$

10. $(x + 4)^2 + (y − 3)^2 = 25; y = x + 2$
    (−4, −2), (1, 3)

11. **EARTHQUAKES** When an earthquake strikes, it releases seismic waves that travel in concentric circles from the epicenter of the earthquake. Seismograph stations monitor seismic activity and record the intensity and duration of earthquakes. Suppose a station determines that the epicenter of an earthquake is located about 50 kilometers from the station. If the station is located at the origin, write an equation for the circle that represents one of the concentric circles of seismic waves of the earthquake.
    $(x − 50)^2 + y^2 = 2500$

NAME _____ DATE _____ PERIOD _____

10-8 Word Problem Practice

Equations of Circles

1. **DESIGN** Arthur wants to write the equation of a circle that is inscribed in the square shown in the graph.

   What is the equation of the desired circle?
   $(x − 4)^2 + (y − 3)^2 = 4$

2. **DRAFTING** The design for a park is drawn on a coordinate graph. The perimeter of the park is modeled by the equation $(x − 3)^2 + (x − 7)^2 = 225$. Each unit on the graph represents 10 feet. What is the radius of the actual park?
   150 ft

3. **WALLPAPER** The design of a piece of wallpaper consists of circles that can be modeled by the equation $(x − a)^2 + (y − b)^2 = 4$, for all even integers b. Sketch part of the wallpaper on a grid.
   Sample answer:

4. **SECURITY RING** A circular safety ring surrounds a top-secret laboratory. On one map of the laboratory grounds, the safety ring is given by the equation $(x − 8)^2 + (y + 2)^2 = 324$. Each unit on the map represents 1 mile. What is the radius of the safety ring?
   18 mi

5. **DISTANCE** Cleo lives the same distance from the library, the post office, and her school. The table below gives the coordinates of these places on a map with a coordinate grid where one unit represents one yard.

Location	Coordinates
Library	(−78, 202)
Post Office	(111, 193)
School	(202, −106)

   a. What are the coordinates of Cleo's home? Sketch the circle on a map locating all three places and Cleo's home.
      (7, −2)

   b. How far is Cleo's house from the places mentioned?
      221 yd

   c. Write an equation for the circle that passes through the library, post office, and school.
      $(x − 7)^2 + (y + 2)^2 = 221^2$

NAME _____ DATE _____ PERIOD _____

10-8 Enrichment

Equations of Circles and Tangents

Recall that the circle whose radius is r and whose center has coordinates (h, k) is the graph of $(x - h)^2 + (y - k)^2 = r^2$. You can use this idea and what you know about circles and tangents to find an equation of the circle that has a given center and is tangent to a given line.

Use the following steps to find an equation for the circle that has center $C(-2, 3)$ and is tangent to the graph of $y = 2x - 3$. Refer to the figure.

1. State the slope of the line l that has equation $y = 2x - 3$.

   2

2. Suppose $\odot C$ with center $C(-2, 3)$ is tangent to line l at point P. What is the slope of radius $\overline{CP}$?

   $-\dfrac{1}{2}$

3. Find an equation for the line that contains $\overline{CP}$.

   $y = -\dfrac{1}{2}x + 2$

4. Use your equation from Exercise 3 and the equation $y = 2x - 3$. At what point do the lines for these equations intersect? What are its coordinates?

   $P; (2, 1)$

5. Find the measure of radius $\overline{CP}$.

   $\sqrt{20}$ or $2\sqrt{5}$

6. Use the coordinate pair $C(-2, 3)$ and your answer for Exercise 5 to write an equation for $\odot C$.

   $(x - (-2))^2 + (y - 3)^2 = 20$ or $(x + 2)^2 + (y - 3)^2 = 20$

Chapter 10 Assessment Answer Key

Quiz 1 (Lessons 10-1 and 10-2)
Page 57

1. _____8_____

2. ____40.84 in.____

3. _____73_____

4. ____6.28 in.____

5. _____D_____

Quiz 2 (Lessons 10-3 and 10-4)
Page 57

1. _____70_____

2. ____15 in.____

3. _____22_____

4. ____90, 40____

5. _____120_____

Quiz 3 (Lessons 10-5 and 10-6)
Page 58

1. ____$12\sqrt{3}$ ft____

2. _____false_____

3. _____77.5_____

4. _____75_____

5. _____90_____

Quiz 4 (Lessons 10-7 and 10-8)
Page 58

1. _____4_____

2. ____$x = \sqrt{21},\ y = \dfrac{17}{2}$____

3. ____(−11, 13)____

4. _____15_____

5.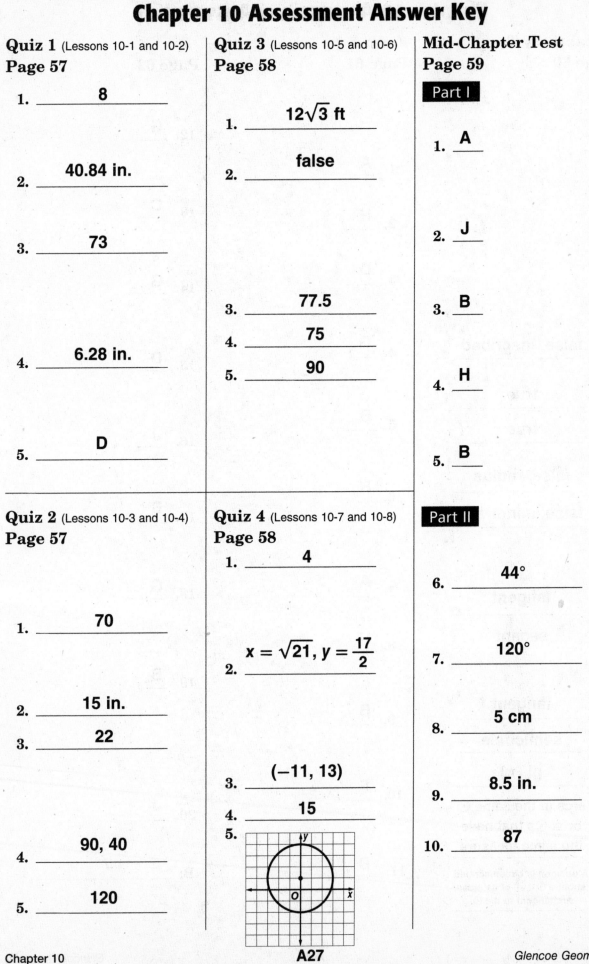

Mid-Chapter Test
Page 59

Part I

1. _A_

2. _J_

3. _B_

4. _H_

5. _B_

Part II

6. _____44°_____

7. _____120°_____

8. _____5 cm_____

9. _____8.5 in._____

10. _____87_____

Answers

Chapter 10 Assessment Answer Key

Vocabulary Test
Page 60

Form 1
Page 61

Page 62

1. false, inscribed

2. true

3. true

4. false, radius

5. false, minor arc

6. tangent

7. secant

8. tangent

9. semicircle

10. pi (π)

11. arcs in the same ⊙ or ≅ ⊙s that have the same measure

12. A polygon is circumscribed about a ⊙ if all of its sides are tangent to the ⊙.

1. A

2. H

3. D

4. G

5. B

6. H

7. A

8. H

9. B

10. F

11. D

12. G

13. C

14. G

15. D

16. J

17. B

18. G

19. B

20. J

B: 7

Chapter 10 Assessment Answer Key

Form 2A
Page 63

1. __A__
2. __G__
3. __C__
4. __F__
5. __C__
6. __G__
7. __C__
8. __J__
9. __D__
10. __F__
11. __D__

Page 64

12. __H__
13. __C__
14. __F__
15. __B__
16. __J__
17. __B__
18. __F__
19. __D__
20. __F__

B: _____10_____

Form 2B
Page 65

1. __B__
2. __H__
3. __C__
4. __F__
5. __C__
6. __F__
7. __B__
8. __H__
9. __C__
10. __F__
11. __B__   B: ____outside____

Page 66

12. __H__
13. __A__
14. __H__
15. __A__
16. __J__
17. __C__
18. __J__
19. __D__
20. __G__

Answers

Chapter 10 Assessment Answer Key

Form 2C

Page 67

1. _____ 2 in. _____

2. _____ radius = 5.5 in. and diameter = 11 in. _____

3. _____ 80° _____

4. _____ 15.71 units _____

5. _____ 7 _____

6. _____ 12 m _____

7. _____ 52 _____

8. _____ 36° _____

9. _____ $\dfrac{4}{5}$ _____

10. _____ 7 units _____

11. _____ 11 _____

Page 68

12. _____ $\dfrac{7}{3}$ _____

13. _____ 31° _____

14. _____ 41° _____

15. _____ 70° _____

16. _____ 100° _____

17. _____ $2\sqrt{2}$ _____

18. _____ $(x - 3)^2 + (y - 5)^2 = 26$ _____

19. _____ $(x + 4)^2 + (y + 9)^2 = 100$ _____

20.

B: _____ $y = -\dfrac{4}{3}x + \dfrac{23}{3}$ _____

Chapter 10 Assessment Answer Key

Form 2D
Page 69

1. _____4_____

2. ____62.8 in.____

3. _____29_____

4. ___75.40 units___

5. _____90°_____

6. _____$\frac{29}{4}$_____

7. _____96_____

8. _____80°_____

9. _____$-\frac{3}{5}$_____

10. ____9 units____

11. _____11_____

Page 70

12. _____7_____

13. _____60°_____

14. _____70°_____

15. _____50°_____

16. _____110°_____

17. ___$(x + 7)^2 + (y - 8)^2 = 81$___

18. ___$(x - 4)^2 + (y + 9)^2 = 116$___

19. _____$3\sqrt{5}$_____

20.

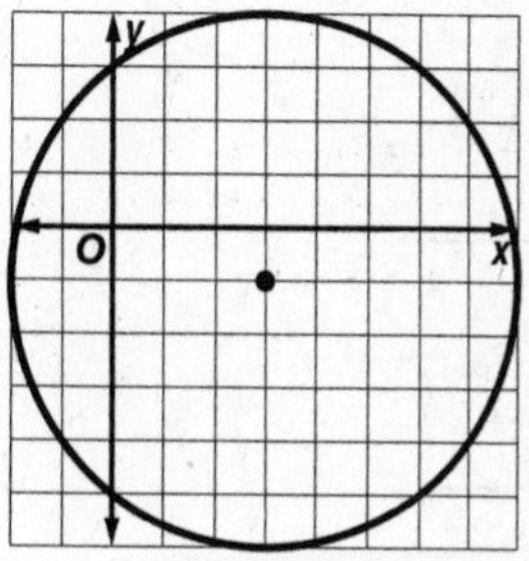

B: ___$(-1, 2), (-1, -2)$___

Answers

Chapter 10 Assessment Answer Key

Form 3
Page 71

Page 72

1. $3\sqrt{2}$ ft

2. 26.66 in.

3. 149°

4. 27 in.

5. $4\sqrt{6}$

6. 17 cm

7. 47

8. $\dfrac{\sqrt{2}}{2}$ ft

9. $\dfrac{10\sqrt{3}}{3}$

10. 4

11. 58

12. 25°

13. 62.5°

14. 52.5°

15. 12

16. 2

17. $(0, 5), \left(\dfrac{300}{61}, \dfrac{55}{61}\right)$

18. $(x + 3)^2 + (y + 2)^2 = 9$

19. center: (6, −7), radius: 9

20.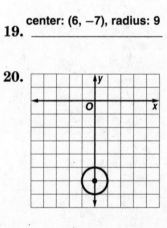

B: (5, 5)

Chapter 10 Assessment Answer Key

Extended-Response Test, Page 73
Scoring Rubric

Score	General Description	Specific Criteria
4	**Superior** A correct solution that is supported by well-developed, accurate explanations	• Shows thorough understanding of the concepts of *circles, arcs, chords, tangents, secants, inscribed and circumscribed polygons, and equations of circles.* • Uses appropriate strategies to solve problems. • Computations are correct. • Written explanations are exemplary. • Figures and graphs are accurate and appropriate. • Goes beyond requirements of some or all problems.
3	**Satisfactory** A generally correct solution, but may contain minor flaws in reasoning or computation	• Shows an understanding of the concepts of *circles, arcs, chords, tangents, secants, inscribed and circumscribed polygons, and equations of circles.* • Uses appropriate strategies to solve problems. • Computations are mostly correct. • Written explanations are effective. • Figures and graphs are mostly accurate and appropriate. • Satisfies all requirements of problems.
2	**Nearly Satisfactory** A partially correct interpretation and/or solution to the problem	• Shows an understanding of most of the concepts *of circles, arcs, chords, tangents, secants, inscribed and circumscribed polygons, and equations of circles.* • May not use appropriate strategies to solve problems. • Computations are mostly correct. • Written explanations are satisfactory. • Figures and graphs are mostly accurate. • Satisfies the requirements of most of the problems.
1	**Nearly Unsatisfactory** A correct solution with no supporting evidence or explanation	• Final computation is correct. • No written explanations or work shown to substantiate the final computation. • Figures and graphs may be accurate but lack detail or explanation. • Satisfies minimal requirements of some of the problems.
0	**Unsatisfactory** An incorrect solution indicating no mathematical understanding of the concept or task, or no solution is given	• Shows little or no understanding of most of the concepts of *circles, arcs, chords, tangents, secants, inscribed and circumscribed polygons, and equations of circles.* • Does not use appropriate strategies to solve problems. • Computations are incorrect. • Written explanations are unsatisfactory. • Figures and graphs are inaccurate or inappropriate. • Does not satisfy requirements of problems. • No answer given.

Copyright © Glencoe/McGraw-Hill, a division of The McGraw-Hill Companies, Inc.

Answers

Chapter 10 Assessment Answer Key

Extended-Response Test, Page 73

Sample Answers

In addition to the scoring rubric found on page A33, the following sample answers may be used as guidance in evaluating open-ended assessment items.

1. 100 families were surveyed about the type of pet they own. The results are:

no pets	20	$\frac{20}{100} = \frac{x}{360}$	72°
dogs	30	$\frac{30}{100} = \frac{x}{360}$	108°
cats	25	$\frac{25}{100} = \frac{x}{360}$	90°
fish	15	$\frac{15}{100} = \frac{x}{360}$	54°
birds	10	$\frac{10}{100} = \frac{x}{360}$	36°

Pie chart:
- cat 25%
- no pets 20%
- fish 15%
- dog 30%
- bird 10%

2a. Arc length is the measure of the distance around part of a circle. It is a fraction of the circumference of the circle. Arc length is measured in centimeters or inches or feet, etc. Arc measure is the number of degrees in an arc. It is measured with a protractor.

2b. Yes. The arcs could have the same measure, for example 60, but could be arcs in circles with different radii. The arc in the circle with the greater radius would have a greater length.

3.

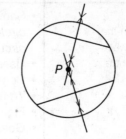

4. The measures decrease.

5a. $(x - 2)^2 + (y + 3)^2 = 25$

5b. $B(-1, 1)$

5c. center: $(2, -3)$

The slope of the segment, having endpoints at B and the point of tangency to the center, is $-\frac{4}{3}$. The slope of tangent line is $\frac{3}{4}$. equation: $y - 1 = \frac{3}{4}(x + 1)$ or $y = \frac{3}{4}x + \frac{7}{4}$

Chapter 10 Assessment Answer Key

Standardized Test Practice
Page 74

Page 75

1. Ⓐ Ⓑ ● Ⓓ

2. Ⓕ ● Ⓗ Ⓙ

3. ● Ⓑ Ⓒ Ⓓ

4. ● Ⓖ Ⓗ Ⓙ

5. Ⓐ Ⓑ ● Ⓓ

6. Ⓕ ● Ⓗ Ⓙ

7. Ⓐ Ⓑ Ⓒ ●

8. ● Ⓖ Ⓗ Ⓙ

9. Ⓐ Ⓑ ● Ⓓ

10. Ⓕ ● Ⓗ Ⓙ

11. Ⓐ Ⓑ ● Ⓓ

12. 74

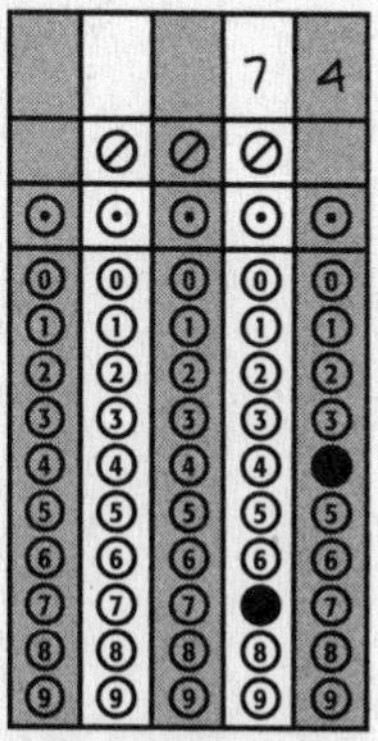

13. 97

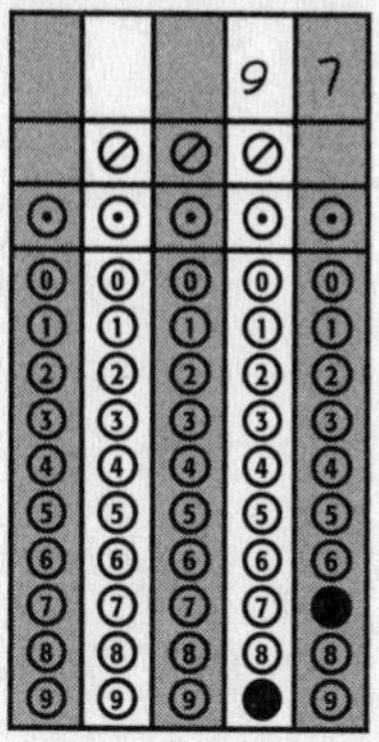

Answers

Standardized Test Practice (*continued*)
Page 76

14. _____ 13° _____

15. _____ $AB > BC$ _____

16. _____ yes _____

17. _____ 20 cm _____

18. _____ true _____

19. _____ $DFHJB \sim PQRJH$ _____

20. _____ $a = 2; b = 20$ _____

21 a. _____ $(x - 4)^2 + (y + 1)^2 = 144$ _____

   b. _____ 24π units _____

   c. _____ 144π units^2 _____